D&T CHALLENGES

COURSE GUIDE

A CTC Trust programme sponsored and
supported by the Royal College of Art,
the Esmée Fairbairn Trust and the
Department for Education

Hodder & Stoughton

A MEMBER OF THE HODDER HEADLINE GROUP

A catalogue record for this title is available from the British Library.

ISBN 0 340 63923 7

First published 1995
Impression number
10 9 8 7 6 5 4 3 2 1
Year
1999   1998   1997   1996   1995

Typeset by Wearset, Boldon, Tyne and Wear.
Printed in Great Britain for Hodder & Stoughton Educational, a division of Hodder Headline Plc, 338 Euston Road, London NW1 3BH by Redwood Books, Trowbridge, Wilts.

CONTENTS

Foreword   5

Introduction   9
The Project's principles   9
What you will find in the students' books   10
What you will find in the *Teacher's Resources*   11
Units, DMAs, FPTs and product evaluations   13
Making a course out of the Units   14
Resourcing the course   17

The Curriculum Model   18
Spiral curriculum learning model   20
Moving on from Key Stages 1 and 2 InSET   22
Summary of National Curriculum changes in
    1995 in D&T   24
Support and Guidance from the Schools Curriculum
    and Assessment Authority (SCAA)   25

Operating the Curriculum Model   27
Mapping the curriculum   27
Planning a year's Units InSET   29
How to choose the Units for your school   31
Recommendations to senior managers   35

The Teaching and Learning Model   37
The students' experience   37
Different routes through for individual students   37
Differentiation InSET   39
Teacher interventions InSET   45
Progression   47

Assessment and the National Curriculum   54
Mapping NC requirements against the Project's
    approach to assessment   54
The RCA STP assessment scheme InSET   55
Assessing capability in D&T   60

Pulling D&T Together InSET   61

FOREWORD

The Royal College of Art has been at the forefront of design and therefore the use and development of technologies for a century now. It has also played a very significant part in developing understanding of the value of design-based approaches to teaching and learning in schools.

It was with great pleasure therefore that we joined with the City Technology Colleges Trust in setting up the Schools Technology Project, and an even greater pleasure to see these first materials from the Project.

Design and Technology together:

> create the products people need
> create products which work well for people
> create products people will buy
> create a buoyant economy.

Future adults – those in our schools now – must understand these things, and from amongst them must come our future designers and technologists. This, though, will only happen with good teaching and commitment to learning. I am sure that the materials produced by the Schools' Technology Project will help Design and Technology thrive in schools and colleges to ensure that this happens.

It is with these thoughts in mind that I commend these materials to you, and am proud to associate the name of the College with them.

Professor Anthony Jones, Rector, The Royal College of Art.

PROJECT TEAM

David Perry Project Director. Formerly Head of Design and Technology at King Alfred's College, Winchester

Louise Davies Deputy Project Director. Formerly Senior Lecturer in Technology teacher education at South Bank University, London

Maria Kyriacou Project Assistant. Formerly worked in IT recruitment

Alan Booth Head of Technology at Wymondham College, Wymondham

Claire Buxton Design and Technology (CDT) Teacher at City and Islington College, London

Anne Constable Head of Design Faculty at the Beauchamp College, Leicester

Corinne Harper Head of Technology Cluster at Burntwood GM School for Girls, London

Dai James Second in Faculty of Technology at Ashfield School, Kirby-in-Ashfield

PROJECT TEAM

Mary Moran Design and Technology Co-ordinator at Kingsway School, Cheadle

Barbara Mottershead Head of Technology Faculty at Shevington High School, Wigan

Robin Pellatt Head of Technology at Bishop David Brown School, Woking

Rob Petrie Head of Design and Technology at St Thomas High School, Exeter

Richard Pinnock Technology Co-ordinator at Vale of Catmose College, Oakham

Brian Russell Senior Manager/R&D, Design, Technology and Art at Dixons CTC, Bradford

Kalvin Turner Head of Design Faculty at Bosworth College, Desford

INTRODUCTION

The Royal College of Art Schools Technology Project (RCA STP) publishes material to support a cohesive and progressive course in design and technology throughout the secondary age range, 11–18. This book gives an overview of the first part of the course; Key Stage 3 of the English and Welsh Design and Technology (D&T) curriculum. Separate students' books, *D&T Challenges* red, green and blue, are provided for Y7, Y8 and Y9 each of which is accompanied by a *Teacher's Resource*. Materials for the 14–16 and 16–18 age ranges will follow.

The course has been founded on a set of thoroughly researched principles which are reflected in the structure of the course as a whole, and every constituent part.

The Project's principles

The Project aims to meet and go beyond the demands of the 1995 National Curriculum through a course which:
- is relevant to adult worlds of design and technology
- acknowledges, and develops from, a prior learning base
- is meaningful to children in today's and tomorrow's world
- supports attention to individual's needs and potential
- stretches to the limit those with most ability, and serves as well all others
- progressively builds in students
  - capability
  - responsibility
  - autonomy
  - awareness and understanding of, and pride in, their own learning
  - knowledge and understanding
  - awareness of others' needs
  - understanding of how Design and Technology activities affect others
  - creativity
  - sensitivity
  - self-confidence
- makes a technologically complex mode of living approachable
- draws in, and makes useful and meaningful, matter studied in other subjects, especially science, maths and art
- draws out the relationship between the nature of designing and learning
- encourages teachers to work together.

The 1995 Statutory Orders for Design and Technology refer to three ways in which students should develop their D&T capability: designing and making assignments (DMAs), focused practical tasks (FPTs), and product investigation/evaluation.

What you will find in the students' books

There are three *D&T Challenges* books in the Key Stage 3 course, one for each year group. The books are intended to fulfil the requirements of National Curriculum Design and Technology.

In each book there are two sections:
1 **Challenges** – these are Units of work which contain designing and making assignments, focused practical tasks and activities involving products and applications.
2 **Designing skills** – this section provides information and activities to support 'process' aspects of all Challenges.

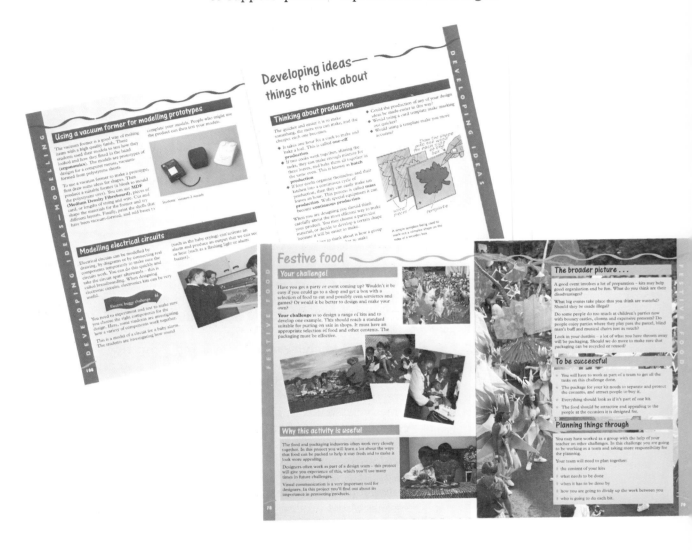

Figure 1: Spreads from a *D&T Challenges* book showing a Challenge and a designing skills section

The content of each book is designed to ensure:
- progression in skills and knowledge and increased demands placed upon students
- coverage of all National Curriculum requirements
- balanced and broad range of experience
- choice for schools to maximise their resources.

The features of the books are as follows:

Y7 Book 1 (red)
- Builds on KS2 skills and knowledge
- Offers orientation activities to familiarise students with their new school environment

- Develops basic skills and helps students to understand the expectations of the teacher
- Activities use a selected range of equipment, materials and components
- Students engage in designing products for themselves and work from personal experience
- Students gain early experience of manufacturing and product development at a simple level
- Independence is developed in a structured way

Y8 Book 2 (green)
- Increased student independence and responsibility
- Activities with a wider range of equipment, materials and components
- Students design products for clients and extend personal experience
- Activities develop team work skills
- Students plan their own work with less teacher direction
- Increased range of skills and knowledge

Y9 Book 3 (blue)
- Prepares students for KS4 courses
- Increased quality is demanded in their outcomes
- More sophisticated application of knowledge and skills
- Activities have an industrial focus or are concerned with commercial production
- Students work with increasing autonomy

What you will find in the Teacher's Resources

There are three *Teacher's Resources*, one to accompany each students' book. The guides are divided into two sections:

1 **Support** for the Challenges and Designing skills in the students' book which comprises:
  - comprehensive teacher's notes for each Challenge including suggestions on how you might organise the Challenge, resource lists, assessment scheme and tips from the teachers who have contributed to this project
  - photocopiable sheets which contain a variety of tasks to support the challenges, extension and enrichment activities, and ideas for homework.

2 **Teaching and learning issues**. This section focuses on key issues in Design and Technology teaching and learning. The issues which are addressed in the Y7 *Teacher's Resource* are:
  - Assessment
  - Differentiation
  - Progression

The issues which are addressed in the Y8 and Y9 *Teacher's Resources* are:
  - Gender
  - Industry links
  - Display and presentation
  - Cross-cultural issues
  - Manufacturing
  - Evaluating products and their applications
  - Special Educational Needs

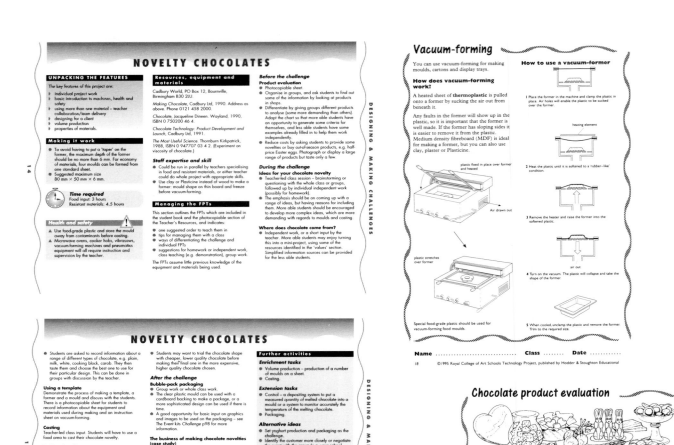

Figure 2: Spreads from a *Teacher's Resource* showing teacher's notes and photocopiable material

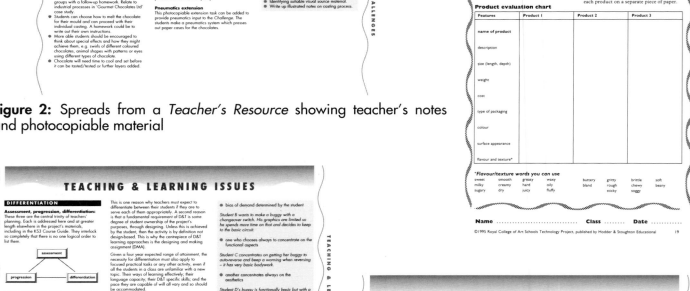

Figure 3: Pages from the Teaching and Learning Issues and Designing Skills sections of a *Teacher's Resource*

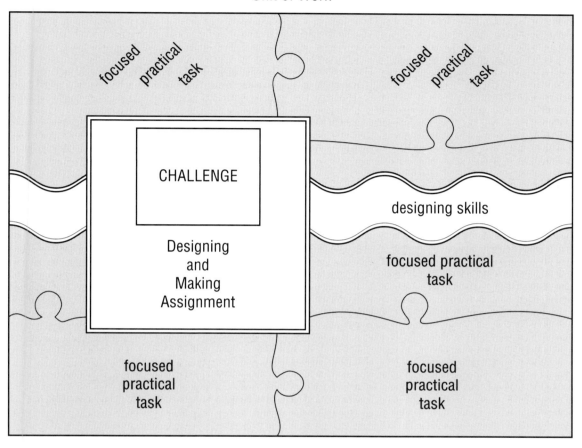

Unit of Work

focused practical task

focused practical task

CHALLENGE

Designing and Making Assignment

designing skills

focused practical task

focused practical task

focused practical task

Figure 4: The composition of a Unit

Units, DMAs, FPTs and product evaluations

The Royal College of Art Schools Technology Project learning approach is constructed around three elements; DMAs, FPTs and product evaluations. Units of learning activities each revolve around a central designing and making assignment. Supporting these are focused practical tasks, which are generally teacher-directed. These can be used as appropriate; preceding, or at points during or after the DMA. In all cases these relate to a specific DMA, though they may be relevant to others.

Product evaluation is used to investigate products which respond to needs similar to those the students are addressing in a DMA. In this case, a product evaluation exercise is presented as an FPT. There are also other times when to investigate products is of general value, e.g. to look at how materials have been used, manufacturing techniques, or design priorities. This type of approach is supported throughout the RCA materials.

Designing and making assignments

These are presented as Challenges, each of which is a rounded or holistic activity which starts from an awareness of needs and clarification of purposes. Each Challenge results in a product, and evaluation of both this and the learning achieved.

The Challenges

These have a number of objectives, they:

- establish the context of the assignment
- give snapshots of similar activities in the adult world
- clarify purposes, giving students ownership of their assignment
- set out initial criteria for success
- explore values issues related to the context
- help teachers and students in setting out a planning framework.

You may have seen some of the Project themes before. But if you concentrate on the approach to teaching which we set out, you will find that it ensures a balance between teacher control over FPTs and a progressive approach to building the all-important independence which is necessary for successful D&T students. You could try using the RCA STP approach with your own familiar projects. Certainly we expect that teachers will 'mix and match' STP Units with projects of their own.

Making a course out of the Units

Teachers will be aware of the constraints imposed on their teaching of D&T by local circumstances. It is unlikely that any follower of the RCA approach will structure his or her programme of study in quite the way that another might. Units will be selected as suitable for the needs of the particular school. Guidance on this is given in the year-by-year *Teacher's Resources* which show the special features of the Units offered each year to help teachers select appropriately. Mapping charts are also included to help teachers ensure that National Curriculum requirements are met.

The basic planning model is shown opposite. This illustrates how different schools might choose different routes through RCA STP material to meet their needs. It recognises that schools will have different starting and finishing points. Some will have the time and resources to go well beyond minimum National Curriculum demands; others will only just meet them.

The first need for any English school will be to meet National Curriculum demands. The most likely problem for many schools will be having enough time available to do only this. Other schools, such as technology colleges, may be using non-National Curriculum time, extending school days or school years to go much further. The features checklists in the Y7, Y8 and Y9 *Teacher's Resources* point out what students can be expected to gain from each Unit included. This allows teachers to select a set of Units with complimentary features.

Much effort has been devoted to showing how individual students and the set of Units available to them should progress in a coherent way, such that higher levels of activity build on basic achievements. The principle is made real – every child's potential is fulfilled.

It must be emphasised that it is of the nature of D&T that the way a Unit is used by a school will have a great deal of influence on the learning outcomes, and every aspect of its value. It will probably have more influence than the particular choice of Units or the way they are presented in RCA STP books.

Chapter 3 of this book gives detailed guidance on planning a course for the Key Stage. This is supported in each *Teacher's Resource* for planning year-by-year.

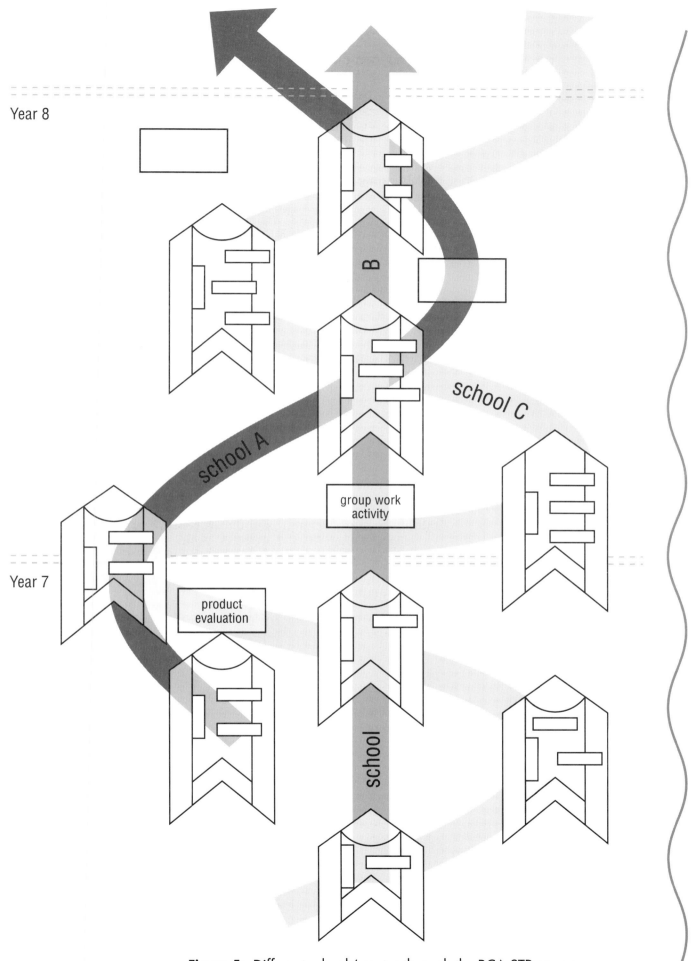

Year 8

Year 7

school A

B

school C

group work activity

product evaluation

school B

Figure 5: Different schools' routes through the RCA STP course

Empowering students

Many of the principles set out at the beginning of the introduction are widely shared in D&T. However, a particular concern of this Project is to enable students to build a sense of ownership; of their learning, of their progress through the course, of the purposes behind their designing and making, and of their future directions.

This is fundamental to D&T. If students are not gaining ownership of their designing and making purposes they are not fully designing but merely going through the motions. This is key to long term success over a D&T course. If a teacher instils in students a sense of engagement and purpose in what they are doing, it becomes more than likely that high quality learning will result, whatever the other constraints, facilities, time or resources. Even the effect of a lack of teacher expertise in a particular area can (to a degree) be reduced if students are supported in owning their learning.

The RCA STP approach at KS3

1 Set up the Challenge in a way which motivates students and allows them to make a personal response, to take ownership of the task. (See the *Why this activity is useful* box on each student DMA spread.)

2 Be flexible, allowing a spontaneous response, so that students can identify and follow their own purposes, pursuing what they think is interesting and creative, valuing it. (Draw attention to the *To be successful* criteria boxes on each student DMA spread.)

3 Allow maximum autonomy, individually or to teams as the task demands.

4 Intervene only when it is in the students' best interests – perhaps in the long rather than short term. Allow constructive failure, ensure eventual success.

5 Emphasise the process skills in designing and underlying knowledge and understanding.

6 Structure the learning such that required skills and knowledge (e.g. from the NC programmes of study) are achieved through active designing and making.

The Project's books emphasise designing skills, as they are core skills in any and every Unit. Whilst the books endeavour to build understanding of the shared concepts behind the equipment and techniques for different materials, making skills are ultimately specific to the task in hand. It is important to acknowledge, though, that understanding the principles behind equipment and techniques helps to develop a transferable approach towards selecting those appropriate to a task.

Resourcing the course

Students' books

The *D&T Challenges* books are designed to help students in a number of specific ways. For example, each Challenge introduction has boxes which share with them:

- the learning purposes behind the Unit – *Why this activity is useful*
- the success (and assessment) criteria – *To be successful*
- guidance on planning their use of time – *Planning things through*
- some of the values issues relevant to the Unit – *The broader picture . . .*

These introductory pages and the following focused practical tasks are useful for students to look at, weighing-up the content together with their teacher.

The Designing skills section is intended to be used for reference. As students become familiar with this section in each book they will gain independence. This helps the teacher, too, allowing more time to select which teaching interventions to make instead of being driven by minute-by-minute student needs.

Therefore sufficient copies of *D&T Challenges* at each level will be needed for students to study the books together with their teacher, and to have for reference.

Teacher's Resources

These support the teacher in two ways. They provide:
1 background guidance and notes,
2 photocopiable worksheets for students.

You will need enough of these for every teacher using the course to have free access.

The Course Guide

This book gives a general overview. There are sections in it with in-school InSET activities which will be particularly useful for those with special responsibility such as heads of departments or co-ordinators.

The book should make a contribution to the professional development of any D&T teacher in enhancing their understanding of the subject and how to teach it well.

Project Papers

Further, more lengthy papers on specific issues, giving insights into the thinking behind the courses, are available from the office at the Royal College of Art Schools Technology Project, Kensington Gore, London SW7 2EU.

THE CURRICULUM MODEL

The basic approach envisaged for a teacher committed to using the RCA STP course is for each year to be structured around learning Units. These comprise designing and making assignments, launched by a Challenge, and supported by focused practical tasks (including product evaluation activities). The focused practical tasks allow individual students to have a variety of experiences throughout the assignment.

Units are in turn carefully structured to provide a framework for the progression of students' learning in a rational manner, through the year and through the key stage.

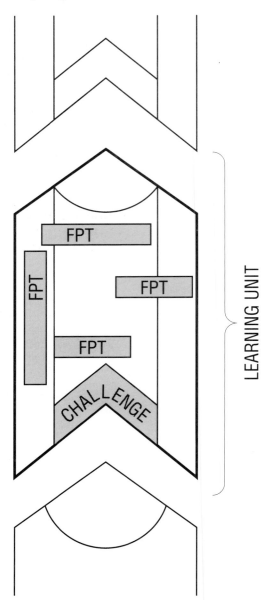

Figure 6: The learning Unit

Whilst the focus of each Unit differs, they are all underpinned by designing process approaches which give students continuity and progression.

The development of designing skills is supported by major sections in each students' book and individual activities within each Unit. Continuity and progression are attended to in depth, both for students and in the *Teacher's Resources*.

Knowledge and understanding are built up through the range of Units undertaken. The Units focus on different contexts and materials, so students develop capability through combining their designing and making skills with knowledge and understanding.

Each Unit has knowledge and understanding associated with the specific context. Some Units are expanded to related science and maths concepts, others reaching into, and drawing on, the Art and Design curriculum. Others enhance cross-curricular capabilities such as IT. These opportunities can be expanded by schools with inter-departmental collaboration, or used to demonstrate transfer of knowledge and skills between subject areas, where appropriate.

Students experience designing and making repeatedly, with Units of varying length, on a spiral curriculum model. This develops their designing and making skills and underpins their knowledge and understanding. Areas of skills and understanding are revisited at progressively higher levels, helping students to consolidate skills from earlier experience and reinforce their skills and understanding. Skills and knowledge are taken further and new aspects are introduced. The Units are designed so that reinforcement takes place, and when a new skill comes to the fore other demands are controlled by the teacher.

Focused practical tasks extend and enrich individual students' learning, providing differentiated learning for all students and the opportunity for each student to reach his or her potential. The most able can be stretched with extension tasks and all abilities can be supported by choosing appropriate focused tasks building an individualised learning programme. Focused practical tasks promote an active way for students to learn new skills and knowledge to help them address the designing and making challenge.

The experience of different students can be expected to differ increasingly across the Key Stage as some stretch to reach their potential and others progress at a more pedestrian rate.

Schools are able to pick and mix Units to make the best use of local conditions, including timetabling and room allocation, specialist facilities and resources, staffing expertise, local community and industry links, and the interests and needs of the students. Some schools have more time and resources and are able to follow an enriched course, teaching more Units and fuller versions of the Units. This may involve extra input and tasks, extension work and collaboration across materials to suit timetabling and staffing expertise. This could include occasional suspended timetables, a 'technology week' or an additional Unit to make fuller use of, for example, electronics/pneumatics facilities at the school.

Other schools will choose a more limited model and will tailor the course to teach the minimum number of Units to fulfil the requirements of the National Curriculum in the time available.

Teacher's Resources provide guidance on the year's Units and on individual Units. Suggestions are given on resources required, learning outcomes, progression and tips from practising teachers on how to manage the Units.

There is always room to respond to special events between or within Units; for example, a Products and Applications exercise to enliven students on the last day before half term, a fast group-work activity of the mini-enterprise variety, incorporating an impromptu celebration or a company presentation into the Unit.

Industrial manufacturing in its widest sense becomes increasingly relevant through the course. If students are to meet the requirements of the KS4 programme of study, such as manufacturing in quantity, they will need to be introduced to this lower down the school. Some Units introduce manufacturing at an appropriate level for Y7 students and increasing attention is paid to this during KS3.

One feature of this course is the use of case studies introducing product development and manufacturing as snap shots and longer case studies. Another is products and applications activities where students evaluate existing products to develop their own criteria.

KS3 experience prepares students for KS4 and underpins a number of possible course options such as GCSE and Part 1 GNVQ. The Units offer a broad and balanced experience for students, including maintaining a range of materials that students work with, so that students may make reasoned choices at the end of Y9.

The RCA STP offers strategies for secondary schools or middle schools moving their students into Y7/Y8 to acknowledge their prior learning and gives guidance about the nature of the changes KS3 brings. It is important that schools build on previous school experience and ensure continuity and progression for individual students, as well as easing the change of schools and learning environment. Guidance is given in the *Course Guide* and *Teacher's Resources* and activities for students are suggested in the students' books.

The RCA STP also supports the planning and management of the curriculum as well as in-school InSET to develop teachers' understanding. InSET activities are provided throughout this *Course Guide* and these can be used in your technology team meetings by the technology co-ordinator, or as self-directed activities.

Spiral curriculum learning model

The RCA STP is committed to a spiral model of learning whereby designing and making are activities repeated in differing contexts, each with its own demands.

The central feature of the spiral curriculum model is that areas of skills and understanding are revisited again and again but at progressively higher levels. By repeatedly covering previously practised aspects of designing and making, students consolidate skills from earlier experience and reinforce their skills and understanding. However, as learning experiences continue, skills and understanding are taken further and new aspects are introduced. The diagrammatic example opposite sketches a number of aspects progressing together – sometimes one aspect moving ahead as it is concentrated on in a DMA, then that aspect consolidating as the focus moves to another. In real life, this process is very complex. Each individual has her or his own learning spiral which is influenced partly by the teacher's management of learning experiences and by a variety of other factors.

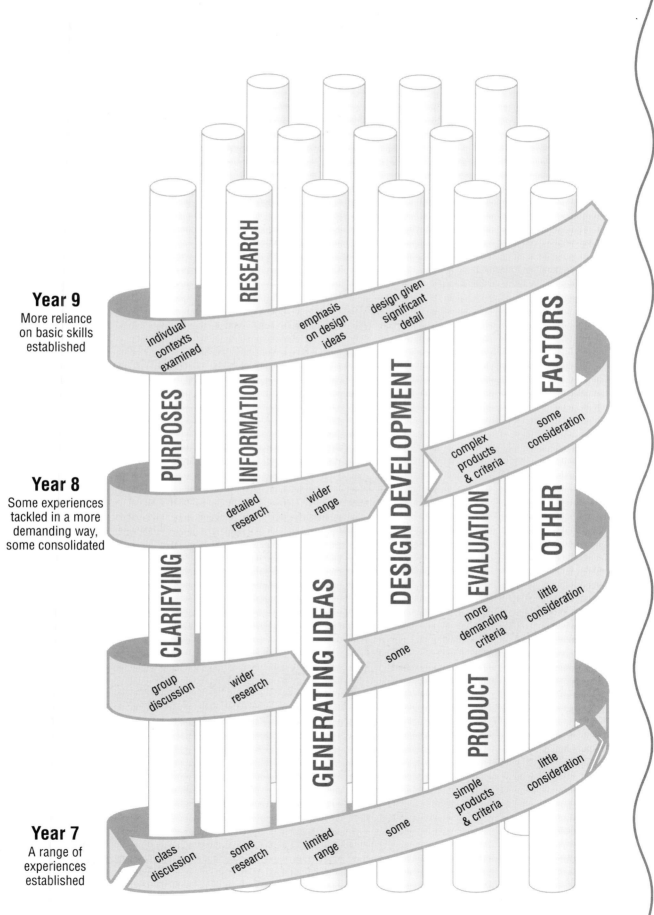

Year 9
More reliance on basic skills established

Year 8
Some experiences tackled in a more demanding way, some consolidated

Year 7
A range of experiences established

Figure 7: Spiral curriculum learning model

Moving on from Key Stages 1 and 2

By the age of 11, our students have been developing their D&T capability in school for six years. Between the ages of 5 and 11, very rapid development takes place and students have a wide range of skills and knowledge on which to base future learning. Whether newly arrived in a secondary school, or continuing in a middle school, students should be ready for a significant 'change of gear' as they move toward greater awareness of the adult world.

It is widely recognised, however, that the experience at KS3 is radically different from that at KS2, and that most students need help in adapting to the new learning environment. Some of the differences are:

- teaching and learning styles
- classroom organisation
- language and conventions used
- assessment and record systems
- resources, equipment and materials
- time available and the way that time is structured.

In most primary and middle schools, D&T is taught through classroom-based topic work. There is usually only a narrow range of specialist equipment and few, if any, specialist teachers or technicians. Specialist rooms are rare. One class with one teacher in the same classroom all week is a common approach.

InSET

Take a moment to consider how different this is from the technology area in a secondary school.
Look at it through the eyes of a new Y7 student.

The RCA STP recognises the potential impact of all this change and offers a variety of mechanisms to ease students' transition from a primary to a secondary school approach and to help ensure a sense of continuity.

Acknowledging learning from KS1 and KS2

Orientation activities (Ready Steady Go)

There is a section of orientation activities in the red *D&T Challenges*. The aims of this section are:

- **The teacher gets to know the students.** For example, students are asked to bring in a piece of D&T work from their previous school to show to the class. This can be an opportunity to find out some skills and knowledge they already have, which can be built on in Y7 Challenges. This helps the teacher with planning but also makes the students feel that their experience is valued.
- **Students share what they can do already.** For example, the students have an opportunity to look at activities in the students' book which are similar to ones they might have experienced in their primary school. This can make students feel comfortable. Licence activities – tests for using the sewing machine, cooker, pillar drill or other equipment – acknowledge what students can do already and encourage independence and a sense of accomplishment.
- **Students are introduced to their new environment and activities they are likely to be doing.** For example, they could be introduced to the staff and facilities and have initial procedures explained to them: where to go to get help, how to get ready for work and look after their work, how to manage their time and so on. This helps them to become familiar with their new environment and what is expected of them.

Post-orientation activities (Puppets, Wall Hanging and Novelty Chocolates)

The introductory Y7 Challenges use a range of learning strategies which allow students to demonstrate their abilities and achieve successful outcomes. They incorporate aspects of primary school methods and approaches to make students feel comfortable. At the same time, they introduce the students to the more sophisticated approaches used in secondary school. These Challenges give students the opportunity to work in open-ended ways and, therefore, offer scope for differentiation and allow students to show progression. As a result, they can be used as diagnostic tools.

Using FPTs to differentiate work

When a teacher introduces a Challenge, it should become apparent what knowledge and skills students have brought with them from KS2 that will support the Challenge. This experience may not be shared by the whole class, especially if students have come from different schools. In these cases a refresher activity can be provided for those students who need it. (e.g. the *Door Buzzer* Challenge and *Electricity* refresher task).

The following checklist may be helpful when introducing an activity:
- Is this activity appropriate for these students at this time?
- Is it necessary to repeat it? If so, when and how?
- Is it reinforcement?
- Will the activity lead to confusion?
- How can I prepare the students?
- What should be the follow-up?
- In what ways does this activity relate to previous ones and those to follow?

Links to primary schools

Links between primary and secondary schools are something that most teachers support, yet often do not have the time to establish or maintain. It is made more difficult for a school with a large number of feeder primary schools. These links would help to avoid duplication of project content, and could lead to development of a project which starts in the primary school and is then continued in the secondary school. Different teachers and different schools, who have responsibility for the same students over a period of time, need to work together to ensure a continuity of experience for all students.

Consider in your school how you could develop closer links with your feeder primary schools. You could:
- visit feeder primary schools, talk to primary teachers
- offer opportunities for primary students to visit and take part in your classes
- ask students to bring samples of primary work to lessons – folders and things they have made or photos to help teachers and fellow students appreciate work they have done previously
- study students' records and assessment profiles to help you to identify students who may need extra help and those who may need to be stretched.

Summary of National Curriculum changes in 1995 in D&T

Comparison of 1990 and 1995 Orders

1995 Orders	1990 Orders
Pupils develop their D&T capability through: ● assignments in which they design and make products, focusing on different contexts and materials, including the use of – resistant materials compliant materials and/or food ● focused practical tasks in which they develop and practise particular skills and knowledge ● activities in which they investigate, disassemble and evaluate familiar products and applications	*Students should:* ● design and make – artefacts systems environments ● work in contexts e.g. home, school, recreation, community, business and industry ● work with a range of materials including textiles, graphic media, construction materials and food

D&T is a practical subject in which students design and make products. Both the 1990 and 1995 orders are very clear about this central tenet of the subject. The new Order has eliminated a great deal of prescription. It has introduced clear guidelines about the kinds of activities students should be engaging in. The Order intends that students develop knowledge and understanding of existing products through investigating, disassembling and evaluating products to help them design and make new ones. This represents a move from 'what is' to 'what might be'. In KS3 RCA STP materials we have approached product evaluation in two ways. Firstly, there are case studies to help students develop evaluation criteria for their own products. Secondly, there are focused practical tasks to investigate and evaluate existing products.

Attainment targets

1995 2 attainment targets: ● Designing ● Making	**1990** 5 attainment targets: ● Identifying needs and opportunities ● Generating a design ● Planning and making ● Evaluating ● IT capability

The absorption of the former ATs 1 and 4 into the two attainment target model does not mean that *identifying needs and opportunities* and *evaluation* are no longer important D&T processes. Good D&T capability will be developed from identifying real needs. Evaluation is elevated from something that occurred at the end of an activity to an on-going process throughout designing and making. IT, the former AT5, now stands alone as a cross-curricular concern with a common requirement that 'pupils should be given opportunities, where appropriate' to develop and apply their IT capability in their study of D&T. A number of RCA STP Units offer such opportunities within KS3.

1995 8 level descriptions	**1990** 10 levels of statements of attainment

The function of level descriptions is 'to assist in making summary judgements about pupils' achievement as a basis for reporting at the end of a key stage'. As students should not be judged on level descriptions before they have completed the programme of study, RCA STP has devised its own scheme for interim assessment. A full explanation of the role of assessment is given both in this *Course Guide* and also in the *Teacher's Resource* for each year.

Support and guidance from the Schools Curriculum and Assessment Authority (SCAA)

The 1995 Statutory Order for D&T provides only an outline framework within which schools are obliged to work. How they do this is at their discretion and will depend on local circumstances.

The SCAA publishes a support and guidance document, called *D&T: The new requirements*, which goes some way to illustrating approaches which schools can adopt. The RCA STP aims to expand significantly this guidance and support teachers in far greater depth. The course is based on a detailed rationale which has been brought to a fully operational state by practising teachers and the central Project team.

The RCA course extends beyond the minimum requirements of the National Curriculum. It provides activities which will retain coherence if numerous learning Units are used and the most adventurous approaches adopted. By this means it will be suitable for adoption by the whole spectrum of schools, from those with the most to those with the least resources for D&T.

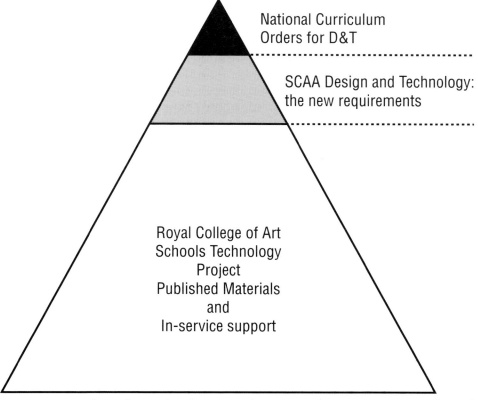

National Curriculum Orders for D&T

SCAA Design and Technology: the new requirements

Royal College of Art Schools Technology Project Published Materials and In-service support

Figure 8: The relationship between the NC Order, SCAA materials and the RCA STP

KS4 materials from the Project provide for the needs of a range of examination syllabuses across academic and vocational routes. Later materials, going beyond the age of statutory schooling, are also designed for use in Further Education institutions.

In-service support activities for schools and colleges are available, and continue throughout the life of the RCA STP.

OPERATING THE CURRICULUM MODEL

The Royal College of Art Schools Technology Project does not take one single approach to managing the D&T curriculum. We recognise that schools vary greatly in size, staffing, resourcing, and the nature of the student population and their prior experience. Therefore, our curriculum model will be operated differently in each school. We also recognise that schools will adapt some parts of our approach to their existing practices. For these reasons we offer a flexible model and the rationale allows it to be adapted to suit any school's needs.

Among the variations between schools, the availability of staff is probably the most important factor in determining the approach a school will use. Expertise, teaching experiences, ages, ability to work together and the leadership they receive are fundamental to the quality of the D&T curriculum.

Notwithstanding these variations, every school must ensure that the demands of the National Curriculum Orders are fulfilled and that students receive a high quality experience, reaching the best possible standards of achievement. All this needs planning, regular review and revision.

Managing the curriculum experiences of children across the whole of a Key Stage clearly depends on good year-by-year management (which is supported by the *Teacher's Resources*).

Industrial and commercial organisations have learnt that management information systems (MIS) are essential to their success. Without knowing how an organisation is performing, potential improvements cannot be identified or put into practice. Schools, too, need to identify their management priorities so that they can plan, review and revise them. For these reasons we provide you with a chart, or mapping format, to carry out these essential tasks efficiently.

Time is always in short supply. Design and Technology's learning style requires a lot of time. This is why it is so common for D&T teachers to provide their students with lunchtime and after school extensions. Students' time in D&T can thus be used to maximum effect.

No matter what organisational approach is adopted, students' learning experiences must be cohesive. Chapter 5 of this book sets out ways to ensure this.

Mapping the curriculum

The mapping format that follows is designed as both a planning and a reviewing tool, to help schools to select learning Units and to ensure that National Curriculum (1995 Order) requirements are fulfilled. Each unit comprises a central DMA with supporting focused practical tasks (FPTs). The school can decide which emphases are brought to a Unit, how it will be resourced and staffed, and how much time will be devoted to it. This is in part reflected in the FPTs selected.

The curriculum map should be reviewed, perhaps at the end of each term, to confirm progress and review the next Units planned, to ensure that they move on from the point which students have reached.

Figure 9: Blank skills and knowledge map, 1995 Order, KS3 Programme of Study

Activity	Skills		Knowledge and Understanding					
	Designing	Making	Materials	Systems & Control	Structures	Products & Applications	Quality	Health & Safety
	a b c d e f g h i j k l	a b c d e f g h i j k	a b c d e	a b c d e f g	a b c d e f g	a b c d e f	a b c d	a b c

Planning a year's Units

Curriculum planning is a designing activity. Doing it well therefore requires some good 'designerly' approaches:

1. Note the constraints that apply, for example:

Number of students	Staffing available/needed
Rooms/facilities available	Total time per week
Known interruptions (e.g. Sports Days)	Total time per year
Contingency time (for unforeseeable problems)	

2. Draw up a map of the whole year, showing the number of weeks each term with weekly time and rooms available.

Y7	7 RG Mon 1	Tues 5-6	7 RP Mon 5	Thurs 1-2	7 BA Tues 3-4	Fri 1	7 WL Thurs 5	Fri 5-6	ROOM T1	T2	T3	T4	T5	T6	T7	MEDIA SUITE
AUTUMN	O	O	*	*	X	X			O			*				X
	O	O	*	*	X	X			O			*				X
	O	O	*	*	X	X			O			*				X
	O	O	*	France trip	X	X			*				X			O
	O	O	*	*	X	X			*				X			O
	O	O	*	*	X	X			O				X			*
	O	O	*	*	X	X			O				X			*
	O	O	*	*	X	X			O			*	X			
CHRISTMAS OUTING																
	O	O	*	*	X	X			O			*	X			
SPRING																
SUMMER																
SPORTS DAY																

Figure 10: Sample year plan

3. Sketch out a possible sequence of Units bearing in mind the need to:
   Balance the use of resources and staff
   Vary blocks of time
   Offer a different pace of work for some students
   Match blocks of time if running discrete Units in different areas.
4. Annotate the sequence in discussion with colleagues, e.g. any potential resource or time scale problems, FPTs that could cross-link areas.
5. Complete the RCA STP curriculum map to check the balance of experiences. Revise the time plan as necessary.
6. Detail activities for the first term.
7. Revise the plan as the end of term approaches and repeat the procedure for the next term.

InSET – Mapping Units of work in KS3

For a 'hands-on' check that you know as a team which NC requirements each Unit will cover, photocopy the KS programmes of study from the Orders and cut them into strips (one per numbered requirement e.g. 3g, 4f, etc.). Put a piece of A3 paper on the floor for each DMA Unit proposed. Throw the strips onto the A3 sheet to represent the NC coverage for that Unit.

Allocating FPTs

Now add notes to the A3 sheet to indicate e.g. what FPTs will be needed to ensure that the necessary teaching input is made to meet NC learning requirements.

Figure 11: Map for Y7 Units

N.C. Skills and Knowledge Map

Activity	Skills																						
	Designing												Making										
	a	b	c	d	e	f	g	h	i	j	k	l	a	b	c	d	e	f	g	h	i	j	k
Novelty Chocolates	*	*	*	*	~	~	*	~	*	*	~	*	*	*	*	*		*	*	~	~	*	*
Puppets	*	*		*	~	*	*	*	*	*	~	*	*	*	*	*	*	*	*		~	*	*
Wall Hanging	*	*	*	*	~	~	*	~	*	*	*	*	*	*	*	*		*	*	~	*	*	*
Door Buzzer	*	*	*	*	~	*	*	~	*	*	*	*	*	*	*	*	*	*	*		~	*	*
Disk Case	*	*		*	~	*	*	~	*	*	*	*	*	*	*	*		*	*	~	*	*	*
Creative Salads	*	*	*	*	*	*	*	*	*	*	*	*	*	*	*	*		*	*		*	*	*
CAD/CAM Puzzle	*	*	*	*	~	*	*	~	*	*	*	*	*	*	*	*		*	*	~	~	*	*
Pasty Product Dev	*	*	*	*	*	*	*	*	*	*	*	*	*	*	*	*		*	*	*	*	*	*
Can Crusher	*	*	*	*	~	*	*	*	*	*	*	*	*	*	*	*		*	*		*	*	*
Electric Buggy	*	*		*	~	~	*	~	*	*	*	*	*	*	*	*	*	*	*		~	*	*
Art Deco Jewellery	*	*	*	*	~	*	*	~	*	*	*	*	*	*	*	*		*	*	~	~	*	*
Event Kits	*	*	*	*	*	*	*	*	*	*	*	*	*	*	*	*		*	*	*	*	*	*

Activity	Knowledge and Understanding																													
	Materials					Systems & Control							Structures					Products & Applications						Quality				Health & Safety		
	a	b	c	d	e	a	b	c	d	e	f	g	a	b	c	d	e	a	b	c	d	e	f	a	b	c	d	a	b	c
Novelty Chocolates	*	*	*	*	*	~				~								*	*	*	*	*	*	*	*	*		*	*	*
Puppets	~	~	*	*	*	~	*	~		~			*					*	*	*	~	*	*	*	*	*	*	*	*	*
Wall Hanging	*	~	*	*									~					*	*	*		*	*	*	*	*		*	*	*
Door Buzzer	*	*	*	*	*	*		*		*								*	*			*	*	*	*			*	*	*
Disk Case	*	*	*	*												*		*	*	*	~	*	*	*	*			*	*	*
Creative Salads	*	*	*	*														*	*	*	*	*		*	*	~		*	*	*
CAD/CAM Puzzle	*	*	*	*														*	*	*	~	*		*	*			*	*	*
Pasty Product Dev	*	*	*	*	~													*	*	*	*	*	*	*	*	~	~	*	*	*
Can Crusher	*	*	*	*		*	*			*			*	*	*		*	*	*	*	*	*		*	*	*	*	*	*	*
Electric Buggy	*	*	*	*	*	*	*	*		*			*	*		*	*	~	~	~		~		*	*			*	*	*
Art Deco Jewellery	*	*	*	*	*					*								*	*	*	*	*	*	*	*			*	*	*
Event Kits	*	*	*	*	*													*	*	*	~	*	*	*	*	*	*	*	*	*

* all aspects addressed
~ some aspects addressed
☐ not addressed

1995 Order
Key Stage 3 Programme of Study

Linking Design and Technology with other subject areas

The NC orders for D&T state that: "pupils should be given opportunities to: apply skills, knowledge and understanding from the programme of study of other subjects, where appropriate including art, mathematics and science". The Units provided for Y7 give opportunities to fulfil these requirements. To this list of subjects should be added Information Technology (IT). Successful cross-curricular integration is not achieved by 'forced marriages' but by people who see the immense benefits that such an approach can give. The table identifies opportunities for exploiting the work of pupils in other subjects to enhance their design and technology work.

Attainment Targets

Science
1. Experimental and Investigative Science
2. Life Processes and Living Things
3. Materials and their Properties
4. Physical Processes

Mathematics
1. Using and Applying Mathematics
2. Number
3. Algebra
4. Shapes, Spares and Measures
5. Handling Data

Art
1. Investigating and Making
2. Knowledge and Understanding

	SCIENCE				I.T.	MATHEMATICS					ART
	1	2	3	4		1	2	3	4	5	1&2
Novelty Chocolates	*		*			*	*		*		*
Puppets	*		*	*							*
Wall Hanging	*		*						*		*
Door Buzzer	*			*	*	*	*				*
Disk Case	*		*		*				*		*
Creative Salads	*	*									
CAD/CAM Puzzle	*				*				*		*
Pasty Product Development	*				*	*				*	
Can Crusher	*	*	*	*		*	*	*	*		
Electric Buggy	*		*		*						*
Art Deco Jewellery	*		*		*						*
Event Kits	*	*			*				*		*

Figure 12: Skills and knowledge map for Science, IT, Maths and Art

How to choose the Units for your school

We do not expect schools to complete all the Units offered in each students' book. Units can be chosen and organised in the way that is most appropriate to the needs of your students and your school.

This will depend on:
- the previous experience of pupils
- staffing and resources (rooms, equipment, community/industry links, expertise)
- the time allocated
- other factors such as the school's timetabling approach, level of co-operative working and so on.

The process set out above will help you to select Units for year groups and check for coverage of National Curriculum requirements and progression in skills and knowledge. But you will also have to ensure that the Units selected and the order in which they are taught results in a course which:
- motivates all students
- takes account of students' interests, gender, culture and ability
- provides a balanced and varied experience
- offers different contexts and a range of materials
- ensures individual progression of skills and knowledge
- gives opportunities to choose appropriate materials
- allows students both to work independently and to develop team skills
- makes best use of your school's staffing and resources
- has a variety of shorter and longer projects.

Burntwood Girls School, Tooting

Context

Burntwood is a grant-maintained girls school of 1500 students, founded in 1986 as part of the schools reorganisation in Wandsworth.

One of the founding principles was the importance of team work and collaboration, and structures were established to support this. For example, block timetabling to facilitate collaboration and diagnostic setting was well established before the National Curriculum. The school initially joined the NDTEF pilot scheme which introduced different techniques for managing the D&T team and the new curriculum.

It is regarded as vital that the team hold common views about D&T, employ common practices and use a common language. The team meet each week during a non-contact period created out of the block timetable. The curriculum is developed in a collaborative way, through team discussion, decisions and approval at the weekly meeting. All members of the team take responsibility for the day-to-day running of one year of the D&T curriculum – preparing, producing and developing syllabuses and materials. They keep a watching brief on the experiences of students in that year and suggest items for the team to discuss, such as project ideas, and problems.

The curriculum is delivered using a variety of strategies. Modules vary in length, and flexibility and variety are planned into each Key Stage. e.g. group work and individual work.

Some modules are totally integrated. Each member of staff in the team teaches the same thing at the same time whatever their specialist subject. These usually cover areas identified as key 'designing skills' experiences. Such modules are carefully planned to retain subject specialist teaching while reinforcing and developing students' and teachers' D&T generalist skills.

Other modules use the NDTEF model of beginning the project with a team of students which then split up to go to specialist areas to complete an agreed part of the group's work, later returning to put the parts together to complete the task. Occasionally there are open-ended modules where students can move between specialist areas.

Yet others are more traditional specialist modules with students working in only one area.

The Y7 Curriculum Plan

Two 35 minute periods out of the total of 26 are spent on technology each week. The groups are block timetabled. Half a year group is taught at a time (5 classes of 27–28 students).

16 hour Unit blocks

Group				
1	2	3	4	5
Autumn Term				
Creative Salads	Wall Hanging	Door Buzzer	Puppets	Can Crusher
Can Crusher	Door Buzzer	Wall Hanging	Creative Salads	Puppets
Spring Term				
CAD/CAM Puzzle	Art Deco Jewellery	Pasty Product Development	Electric Buggy	Disk Case
Disk Case	Electric Buggy	Art Deco Jewellery	CAD/CAM Puzzle	Pasty Product Development
Summer Term				
Event Kits All groups – Team activity using additional health and safety FPT. Teams split to separate specialist areas previously not experienced.				

Figure 13: Burntwood School Y7 National Curriculum skills and knowledge map

N.C. Skills and Knowledge Map

Skills

Activity	Designing												Making										
	a	b	c	d	e	f	g	h	i	j	k	l	a	b	c	d	e	f	g	h	i	j	k
Puppets	*	*		*	~	*	*	*	*	*	~	*	*	*	*	*	*	*	*		~	*	*
Wall Hanging	*	*	*	*	~	~	*	~	*	*	*	*	*	*	*	*		*	*	~	*	*	*
Door Buzzer	*	*	*	*	~	*	*	~	*	*	*	*	*	*	*	*	*	*	*		~	*	*
Disk Case	*	*		*	~	*	*	~	*	*	*	*	*	*	*	*		*	*	~	*	*	*
Creative Salads	*	*	*	*	*	*	*	*	*	*	*	*	*	*	*	*		*	*		*	*	*
CAD/CAM Puzzle	*	*	*	*	~	*	*	~	*	*	*	*	*	*	*	*		*	*	~	~	*	*
Pasty Product Dev	*	*	*	*	*	*	*	*	*	*	*	*	*	*	*	*		*	*	*	*	*	*
Can Crusher	*	*	*	*	~	*	*	*	*	*	*	*	*	*	*	*		*	*		*	*	*
Electric Buggy	*	*		*	~	~	*	~	*	*	*	*	*	*	*	*	*	*	*		~	*	*
Art Deco Jewellery	*	*	*	*	~	*	*	~	*	*	*	*	*	*	*	*		*	*	~	~	*	*
Event Kits	*	*	*	*	*	*	*	*	*	*	*	*	*	*	*	*		*	*	*	*	*	*

Knowledge and Understanding

Activity	Materials					Systems & Control							Structures				
	a	b	c	d	e	a	b	c	d	e	f	g	a	b	c	d	e
Puppets	~	~	*	*	*	~	*	~		~			*				
Wall Hanging	*	~	*	*									~				
Door Buzzer	*	*	*	*	*	*		*		*							
Disk Case	*	*	*	*												*	
Creative Salads	*	*	*	*													
CAD/CAM Puzzle	*	*	*	*													
Pasty Product Dev	*	*	*	*	~												
Can Crusher	*	*	*	*		*	*			*			*	*	*		*
Electric Buggy	*	*	*	*	*	*	*	*		*			*	*		*	*
Art Deco Jewellery	*	*	*	*	*												
Event Kits	*	*	*	*	*												

Activity	Products & Applications						Quality				Health & Safety		
	a	b	c	d	e	f	a	b	c	d	a	b	c
Puppets	*	*	*	~	*	*	*	*	*	*	*	*	*
Wall Hanging	*	*	*		*	*	*	*	*		*	*	*
Door Buzzer	*	*			*	*	*	*			*	*	*
Disk Case	*	*	*	~	*	*	*	*			*	*	*
Creative Salads	*	*	*	*	*		*	*	~		*	*	*
CAD/CAM Puzzle	*	*	*	~	*		*	*			*	*	*
Pasty Product Dev	*	*	*	*	*	*	*	*	~	~	*	*	*
Can Crusher	*	*	*	*	*		*	*	*	*	*	*	*
Electric Buggy	~	~	~		~		*	*			*	*	*
Art Deco Jewellery	*	*	*	*	*	*	*	*			*	*	*
Event Kits	*	*	*	~	*	*	*	*	*	*	*	*	*

- * all aspects addressed
- ~ some aspects addressed
- ☐ not addressed

1995 Order
Key Stage 3 Programme of Study

The RCA STP *D&T Challenges* are written for the whole ability range and, although each student book is intended for a particular year, you may use them with other age groups.

For example, a Y7 Challenge can be adapted to make it more demanding for use with Y8 students.

Y8 Challenges can be used with less able Y9 students or as an introductory Unit if students have not had much previous experience of the area covered in the Challenge.

A Y9 Challenge can be used with Y8 students, particularly more able students, where enhanced curriculum time or resources results in students progressing faster and being more experienced in an area, e.g. electronics.

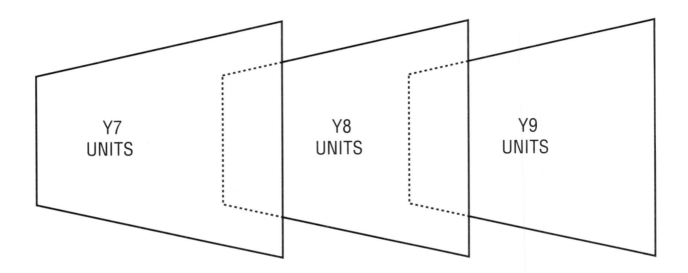

Figure 14: Overlapping Units

The sequence of the Challenges in each students' book broadly reflects the changing demands placed on the student. Thus, Challenges at the end of the book are generally more demanding than those at the beginning. You will need to discuss with colleagues the most appropriate order in which to teach the Units.

There is flexibility in how individual Challenges can be used. The focused practical tasks can support an adapted Challenge, the context can be changed to make it more appropriate to your school, or a different Challenge can be written to make use of a particular community/industrial link.

Once the Units and the FPTs have been allocated across the year, the National Curriculum skills and knowledge map can be completed. This will reveal gaps which can be filled in later years, or adjustments can be made to the current year's programme. In the Burntwood School example, it is clear that the Y7 experience is weak on *Systems and Control* and *Structures*, and that requirements 4e and 4h for *Construction Kits* and *Products in Quantity* have not been met.

Bishop David Brown School, Woking

Context

BDB is an urban neighbourhood comprehensive school with a high proportion of children from minority ethnic groups. The recent change from middle schools in Surrey has made the inclusion of Y7 students a recent experience.

Within the D&T department, students spend the majority of their time working on discrete Units in material-based areas. For part of each year they are involved in Units that require working in more than one specialist area.

When a DMA utilises more than one type of material and requires subject specialists and facilities from more than one area within D&T, detailed planning is essential. The staff involved need to construct a time-plan for their 'subject-specific' content and then collaborate to negotiate a workable time-plan for the DMA.

Novelty Chocolates This DMA requires input from Food and CDT specialists. These inputs – skills and knowledge – have to be delivered at the right time so that specialist activities can take place. In this case, students have a double lesson in CDT followed by a single lesson in Food each week. The time involved is 7.5 hours.

Week 1

CDT

Introduction to the Challenge. Students write their specification, and research materials and equipment needed for the activity.
Homework   Draw initial ideas.

Food

Health and safety, hygiene and conduct. Differences: working with food at home and at school. Need for good co-operation.
Homework   Worksheet on conduct, co-operation and health.

Week 2

CDT

Students develop their design, produce an accurate working drawing and make a template of their design. The template is glued to the balsa and is cut out using a vibrasaw.
Homework   Draw outline on card and add features to produce a 3-D effect on the chocolate, cut them out ready for gluing to the balsa.

Food

Demonstration and knowledge input on microwave cookers. Demonstration of other methods of melting chocolate. Research different types of chocolate.
Homework   Worksheet on chocolate as a food material.

Week 3

CDT

Produce a package design. While this is happening, four students at a time vacuum form their moulds from their balsa and card formers.
Homework   Completion of packaging graphics and draught questionnaire for evaluation.

Food

Demonstration on casting chocolate. Students cast their chocolate bars.
Homework   Testing, recording and evaluating.

NB If the intended time pattern becomes disrupted because of lessons missed, the staff involved need to negotiate readjustment.

This structure can also be used to deliver other Units such as Y7 *Event Kits* (Food and CDT and Graphics).

Recommendations to senior managers

All subject areas within a school demand particular facilities, timetabling, resources and staffing. To operate the curriculum model effectively will require consistent and active support from senior management to identify key staff, facilitate team building, overcome organisational barriers and give an institutional framework to the department/faculty. Senior managers need to understand the nature of the learning experience in Design and Technology.

1 Senior managers and technology teachers need to work together within the overall school development plan. A senior manager may:
   - be attached to oversee and support the work of the technology faculty, including maintaining an awareness of current issues, reading and responding to information provided by the technology team (minutes of meetings, curriculum documents)
   - be involved in D&T curriculum planning to understand the issues and problems, so that technology staff have access to and are able to influence the managerial decisions

- join meetings and discussions on planning
- be the voice which represents D&T at senior staff meetings
- help to raise the profile of technology within the school
- ensure adequate training of staff, adequate resources, appropriate facilities, staff development, appraisal and personal development planning.

2 Senior managers can help prevent restrictive timetabling arrangements and resourcing decisions which do not support learning in D&T by ensuring that:
- timetabling, rooming arrangements and class sizes are appropriate, e.g. manageable class sizes
- year groups are blocked where possible to promote flexible use of time slots, e.g. to allow group visits; large scale presentations to whole year groups; students working in teams; students choosing their own materials and using a range of resources
- faculties work together and team delivery is promoted through timetabled meeting and planning time. Time can be made available for meetings between departments and for joint involvement in InSET programmes
- new ideas are accepted and supported and that 'bottom up' initiatives with release time and supply cover are available when necessary
- the teaching environment is safe, stimulating and accessible.

3 Senior managers can encourage a more consistent approach to equal opportunities, including effective whole school planning, so that learning opportunities are stimulating, challenging and exciting for all students by:
- retaining the range of materials experience, including a broad and balanced experience in resistant and compliant materials, textiles and food, and adequate staffing levels and expertise
- avoiding gender bias
- providing students access to a broad range of resources and the skills required to use them.

4 Senior managers can play an important role as an intermediary between technology teams and school governors by:
- helping their understanding of what the subject is about and the contribution of D&T to educational experience
- inviting them to come to see what is happening in the department on appropriate occasions.

5 Senior teachers may help by opening up channels of communication within the school and with outside organisations, increasing industrial/commercial/community involvement in curriculum matters through:
- links with the community and industry which are valuable for adequate experience of real designing and making activities – real life examples are so much more meaningful to students
- local companies, sponsorship and resources
- promoting the image of the department, information and PR.

THE TEACHING AND LEARNING MODEL

The students' experience

The FPTs within each Unit are generally directed by the teacher and may include:
- a preliminary activity to get the student familiar with the context
- demonstration or teaching of a craft skill
- homework tasks
- didactic teacher input – factual knowledge.

Challenges are set up by the teacher but are driven by the students themselves. Increasing autonomy during the course results in students organising, controlling and directing the learning activity.

A feature of the course is that students have a sense of ownership, of their learning, of their progress through the course, of the purposes behind the DMA and their future directions.

Each Challenge is set up in a way that motivates students, allows them to make a personal response (*Why this activity is useful*), and is flexible enough to encourage students to do what they think is creative and interesting (*To be successful*).

The teacher involves students in planning progress in their own education, encouraging them to take responsibility for their learning. Goals are shared by and with them. There are opportunities for greater autonomy and negotiation as students become ready, and the only way the teacher knows if they are ready is by allowing the students to take the lead and intervening as necessary.

The greatest educational benefit of this approach is that, because students take responsibility for their own learning, it helps them to understand their learning and how to progress – metacognition. Students are encouraged 'to stand outside' of themselves and look objectively at their learning, how well they have done and what they need to do to get better.

Benefits of this approach for the students

The RCA STP course:
- is intellectually stimulating, motivating, enjoyable and interesting
- promotes higher quality learning when students are engaged and see a purpose in what they are doing
- fosters a number of important learning skills – organising their own work, interacting with others, communicating
- provides opportunities for progress, fosters positive attitudes towards themselves as learners and towards the subject
- provides greater insights into the conduct of learning activities by observing others, sharing and discussing procedures and strategies.

Different routes through for individual students

The diagram overleaf shows a group of students working through a Unit. A teacher is faced with the dilemma of having a class of students with a wide range of abilities, the desire to make sure each student is challenged and makes progress in their learning and the need to ensure that the Unit of work is completed within the time block available (for example, 16 hours).

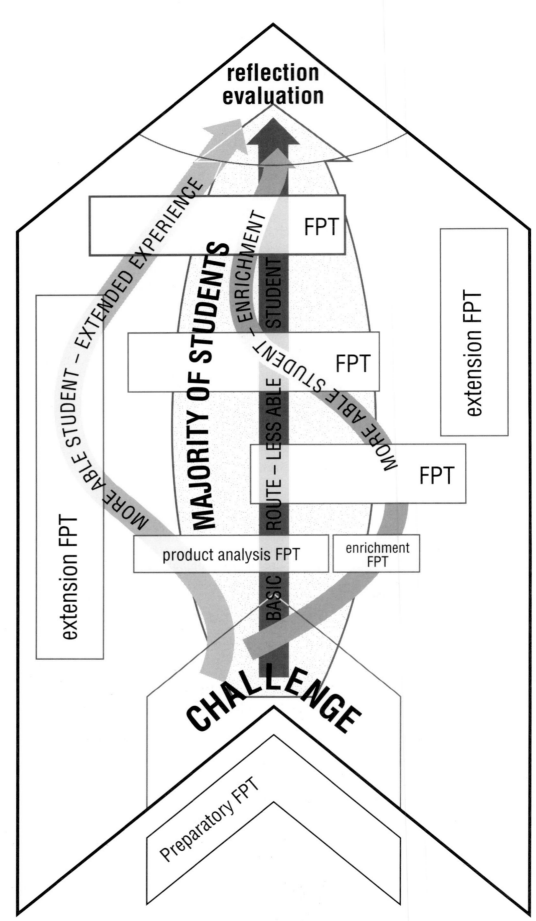

Figure 15: Different students' routes through a Unit

Our approach is based on all students in the same class working on the same Challenge or central activity, with the same starting and finishing point, but that routes taken should be matched to the individual student's interests and ability.

There is a basic entitlement experience for all students (the most direct route through the Challenge), the majority of students will experience a path richer than the basic one.

Some students will be directed to have an enriched experience, doing the same tasks as the rest of the group but with some tasks carried out more fully, to a greater depth and demand, negotiated with the student, but keeping largely the same path as the rest of the group. A teacher can negotiate with a student the aspects of their work which would benefit from enrichment rather than the basic approach. For example, a student who is particularly skilled at research or product evaluation can be expected to carry out a more demanding version of the activity.

A few more able students may be given an extension activity, which makes their path more demanding from the onset and contains activities that are additional and often along a different path from the rest of the group. This prevents a situation where the able student carries out the basic task which is not sufficiently demanding and finishes two weeks ahead of the rest of the group.

The sections which follow explain in more detail the RCA STP teaching and learning model and the approach to:
- Differentiation
- Teacher Interventions
- Progression
- Assessment

Differentiation

Assessment, progression and differentiation are the central trinity guiding teachers' classroom approaches. They interlock so completely that there is no logical order in which to list them. Assessment procedures, so far as they are concerned with individual achievement, are, by definition, concerned with differentiation. To consider the progression of any student, the teacher must assess the student's current position to decide what constitutes progress. The teacher is differentiating simply by recognising that an individual student holds a position different from that of others. Inevitably, each student's progress is different, students have had different learning experiences in life, and have different personalities. Ideally, therefore, teachers should be constantly assessing with students where they are and where they need to go.

To make this manageable, however, we have to lump together students much of the time: in pairs, in small groups, or all too often as whole classes. The only person who can consider the individual's unique position all the time is the student him/herself. For this reason, if for no other, we must involve them as fully as possible in determining how they can progress in the future.

Differentiation, then, is an issue for all teachers. It is rooted in a concern to treat each student as an individual, ensuring that each task undertaken is appropriate for that learner at that point in time.

Individualisation in D&T

D&T is, by its very nature, amenable to differentiated learning activities, especially at the larger project or designing and making activity (DMA) level. A fundamental requirement of D&T is some degree of ownership of the purposes being attended to in a project, through designing. Unless this is achieved by the student, then the activity is by definition not design based.

The first problem for many teachers is that classes are too large for much individual attention and, typically, much of this attention is focused on technical matters – *How to do it* questions. Secondly, many secondary schools do not generally use individual negotiation of purpose and activity widely across the curriculum, so students are not accustomed to this approach. Thirdly, many D&T activities potentially require such a wide range of knowledge and skills such that, if too many were to be needed by the various students, the teacher would be overwhelmed.

This points to the necessity for teachers to build clear working patterns so that students know what is acceptable and what is not; what is expected of them if they are unsure how to proceed; and how much initiative is acceptable (e.g. what level of permission is necessary for them to leave the room to seek information elsewhere). This requirement is one of the reasons why changes of teacher in rotational 'circus' arrangements is so unsatisfactory. The development of students' responsibility for self-direction is both necessary to the 'subject' and to the well-being of the teacher. When achieved, it clears the ground for the teacher to intervene selectively with students to negotiate with them the appropriateness of the demands their work is making on them – a core procedure in differentiation.

Design briefs from the teacher

The restricting of students' freedom is one purpose of a 'design brief' approach to the start of a project. The brief may place specified constraints on them (e.g. the artefact must be made predominantly in wood) or it may direct them into working on something that will be restricted in its demands by its very nature (if a class is set to design a key ring it is very unlikely that any of them will propose anything very large). However, our aim is to build students' experience and independence so that they can make judgements for themselves as to what is feasible or sensible. For this reason the RCA STP approach is to set a Challenge which ideally is as open-ended as possible, although this is less so in the earlier stages of the course.

Typically the D&T teacher's mistake is to limit students' horizons too much, solely as a way of limiting the demands on the teacher, rather than having a conscious strategy to develop individual responsibility. Progressively opening up the amount of control students have over the direction of their work will, on the other hand, encourage students to use their own initiative and take responsibility for their work.

Progression

Study of the nature of progression in D&T suggests that it is characteristically non-linear and (in common with other learning) non-stable and reluctant to transfer. That is, one thing does not necessarily come before another, what is 'known' today may be forgotten tomorrow or its relevance to the new situation may not be realised. Clearly, this complicates the position for the teacher who is seeking to determine whether a student's work is at an appropriate level of demand.

There is also much evidence which suggests that high expectations from teachers (and others) are necessary for students to have high expectations of themselves. These, then, are some of the reasons why successful teaching is a complex art. Central to that art is the ability of the teacher, through their personal interactions with students and through good management of students' activities and learning resources, to help individuals adjust the demands of the work to suit them.

It should be apparent from the above that poor differentiation will result in over- or under-stretched students, under-achievement, bunching of assessment around the norm, disaffected students, low motivation, and a downward spiral in all respects.

Older students

As students mature (which is not necessarily to say as they get older), two factors may follow from the above. Greater reliability in classroom behaviour, greater familiarity with 'how things are done here', more knowledge of skills and techniques, and enhanced ability to direct their own learning all might lead to easing the burden on the teacher in achieving successful differentiation of learning activities.

On the other hand, as they grow older, some students become more disaffected with school. The range of ability and experience of the students in a class is likely to have widened progressively, and many individuals will have become settled with an inaccurate self-picture (e.g. self-fulfilling under-achievement). Adolescence also leads many to be less willing to go out on a limb and risk poor results, playing safe. This is especially true in D&T, as learning activity tends to be very public (if you mess-up what you've been making for the last three weeks your friends are going to notice). All this means that adequate differentiation may be harder to achieve with older students.

How to differentiate approaches to students' learning activities

Three forms of differentiation may be identified in D&T:

1 Differentiation by task
- With a common task (a Challenge) across a group:
  a) the individual level of ambition can be set by the student
  b) the bias in the demands of the task can be determined by the student, for example:
    - one who chooses to concentrate on the function aspects
    - another concentrates on the aesthetics
    - one spends more time on sketching ideas
    - another who rushes into making

- Individual tasks:
  task suited to the student in terms of both type of activity and inherent level of demand – generally achieved through negotiation, distinctly achievable in team work situations.

Teachers are generally hesitant about the feasibility of having students in the same class working on different tasks in the early secondary years. The reasons for this undoubtedly lie in the need to establish new classroom practices (not familiar in primary schools), the fragmented timetable and relative lack of skills of the students. The RCA STP model – introduction, intervention, enrichment, extension – offers ways to differentiate by task within a broad framework of common directions set by the Challenge (see below).

2 Differentiation by process

The best students may show attributes in one of three categories:

- rounded ability in several aspects of the learning/designing process they undertake
- distinctively special ability in key parts of their process
- significant meta-consciousness (taking a clear overview of their process and the reasons why they follow it as they do). This is likely to be confirmed by a good match in appropriateness across the needs, the process and the outcome. That is, the needs are identified clearly, an appropriate course of action is taken and the resultant product fulfils the needs identified. Even in such a scenario, it is possible for the overall achievement to be modest.

Again, there is less chance of students standing out in any of these three respects at KS3.

3 Differentiation by outcome

Some students will achieve better results than others, though of course one might be better in one respect, another in a different respect. This will be the subject of more or less formal assessment by the teacher and of personal evaluation (affecting the student's self-picture). Unless this is the end of the student's formal education, this assessment and evaluation will be carried forward to determine future differentiation.

The RCA STP assessment approach set out later in this section is concerned with emphasising this formative aspect alongside the National Curriculum requirement for summative statements at the end of Key Stages.

Differentiated assessment

Just as teachers must accommodate students' different learning styles, so the approaches to assessment of their learning must also be differentiated. D&T also *requires* varied forms of assessment as it is so varied a subject, utilising a range of skills, knowledge and understanding. Different tasks will vary in their demands on the learner, and any one holistic D&T task will similarly make many, though rarely all, of these demands. For us to assess a DMA by methods which access only one or a few of the responses to these demands will patently be inadequate.

Progression in students' developing capability in D&T will always be multi-dimensional. Criteria for assessment must also therefore be multi-dimensional. In common with most learning, students move ahead and fall back and then move further ahead again, in each and every aspect of design and technological capability (the non-stable factor) as the demands of their work vary. Therefore assessment must be both specific to the task of the moment and, over a period of time, provide an overview or summative picture.

The I-I-E-E Model

For every designing and making activity there are four aspects to consider: introduction, intervention, enrichment and extension.

Introduction

The introduction to a Challenge, especially to ones with tight constraints from the teacher, is crucial. At this stage interest and motivation may be established, or may not. It is not self-evident that certain activities appeal to and interest certain children. With an introduction that is convincing – that convinces the students that it is worthwhile – a project may have a flying start.

Intervention

The purpose of a DMA is that it is more or less student-directed (probably more so later in the secondary school, less so earlier). Without 'ownership' it is merely an exercise. It follows therefore that the teacher's aim is to be 'hands-off', to allow the student to take the lead in determining her or his direction and working method. The teacher's role becomes one of deciding when to intervene, having identified a need to steer a student toward a more profitable direction. In a conversation with an individual, there is a fundamental opportunity for differentiation through the style and level of discourse, the sophistication of thinking engaged in, and the level of difficulty inherent in the direction in which the student is advised to go.

Extension and enrichment

To think in terms of norm plus extension (as many teachers do) is not adequate in D&T. One stage better than this is to extend the work for some and to enrich the work for others. With either approach the result should be an enhancement of the students' learning.

Enrichment

This might mean expecting some students to do more parts of a project, or to do standard parts more thoroughly. Neither of these need take more time. The idea is to give some students who can cope with it a richer experience than others who cannot.

Extension

Extension activities are more closely linked with time. Some students are able to complete the basic requirements of a task more quickly than others. Whilst they may undertake enrichment activities, and thereby utilise their time to greater profit and complete more than others do, an alternative is to extend their horizons with further tasks. There are times when it will be difficult to decide whether the activity adopted is enrichment or extension and it will probably be fruitless to try. However, to ask 'does this take the student further than the basic expectations of the task?' might be useful.

The model

The IIEE model may therefore be portrayed thus.

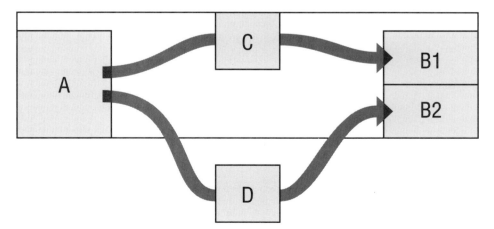

Figure 16: The IIEE model

A represents the starting point for the activity, B1 the end point for one student, and B2 for another student (working faster and completing a further extension). C represents an enrichment activity completed to a better level. D represents an extension activity.

Note that all students, for reasons of class management, may begin and end at the same time, some having done more than others (extensions) and others having done some aspects of the task more thoroughly or in a more sophisticated way (enrichment).

Either extension or enrichment requires students to accept that different members of the same class work to different targets. They are familiar enough with this in the case of differentiation of outcome – they will have seen the results of fellow students who go far beyond the achievements of others. However, it is different if this is formalised with expectations agreed at the start of a project. Some will go well beyond the norm and some stay well within it. This deliberately assumes that it is better that all students, wherever possible, should undertake a rounded activity, from beginning to end, short-cutting or avoiding some demands, rather than abbreviating the task and never finishing anything. This is best planned for from the start.

Typical suggestions from the teacher might be:

You're good at this type of work, Sheila, why don't you have a go at (enrichment or extension activity)?

Ben, you found it difficult to finish the last task, why don't you restrict the amount of record keeping you do on this one and start modelling sooner?

InSET – Differentiation

As a department, set out these guidelines for a familiar DMA.

General guidelines

When planning an activity, plan for differentiation. Ask yourself what minimum and what normal level of result you realistically expect. Ask yourself how you will identify those who might need to work differently from the norm you have in mind. Then consider how the work might be varied to accommodate each of these.

Always look for faster workers to do at least some parts of the work to a higher standard quality. Try to catch them early in the activity and talk them through the value of, for example, better quality research, a wider range of sources, a larger number of initial ideas, more initial testing at the ideas stage, more detailed development of designs, more complex manufacturing techniques, more detailed testing and evaluation.

Plan extension work for those who finish early. Make this relevant to the main activity, extending its value to them. Extension work might include further testing and evaluation, responses to the evaluation such as improvements made to the design, better manufacturing methods, a test piece using more advanced methods, and so on.

Encourage those with better quality ideas to have them evaluated by a wider community – other teachers, parents, other adults, a local industrialist. This can occur before the final direction is determined or whilst a design is being finalised, or after it is modelled in a more developed way (e.g. in a 3D mock-up).

Teacher interventions

The need for variety of teaching style

As students go through the designing and making process during D&T projects they experience several different learning styles:

Aspect of process	Learning style
Identifying purpose	Intuitive, analytical
Initial ideas	Imaginative, creative
Developing ideas	Analytical, inventive
Making	Practical, reflection-in-action
Evaluate	Theoretical, analytical, reflection-on-action

During the Unit teachers will need to adopt teaching styles which complement the learning style in each aspect, which suggests a need for a moment's thought on how, as well as why, to intervene.

Making activities have a teaching tradition which is based on the teacher showing how to do something first, then the students imitating. There is still a place for this teaching style at times. But with the increased range of activities that designing and making brings, teachers need a flexible combination of teaching styles with a complex and subtle balance of direct instruction, guiding, standing back and choosing when to intervene.

It will help if careful planning is undertaken to make sure that the students are familiar with the context of a Challenge, to provide support to help students make decisions at each stage, and equipment and techniques to support students practically in their work.

If much responsibility is given to the students in the first instance, then the decision by the teacher to intervene with a student will have many implications. It must therefore be undertaken carefully.

Why a teacher may intervene:

Intervening for the sake of:
- *better practice*
- *safety*
- *the child*
- *the equipment*
- *the group*
- *speed of progress*

- to correct a student approaching practical work in an unsafe way
- to move students forward, making a suggestion when a student was having problems
- to develop a culture of 'I think before I act'
- to help a group come to a decision or help them work together better
- to provide some new resources for students and teach an important skill
- to develop depth of thinking and understanding (e.g. of the environmental impact of a design)
- to challenge an able student who is taking the easy option (expecting higher standards, setting enrichment or extension work)
- to give help to a less able student

Deciding not to intervene:

Not intervening for the sake of:
- *more independent students*
- *higher expectations*
- *giving space to think*

- learn by mistakes
- think it through
- let students take responsibility for own learning
- not wanting to take task away from students
- reflecting with student on improving approaches, e.g. 'Now let's see how you might have approached this better even without help from me.'
- encouraging students to seek advice from other experts and using more resources, e.g. 'Have you asked Ms Singer, she'll know more than me about that.'

Many of the reasons to intervene listed above will be familiar to D&T teachers, but especially the first one. The more so since step-by-step craft skills teaching ended. The positive side of this is that students are having to think for themselves (at least in the first instance). The negative side to it is that poor practices may be reinforced if the teacher does not intervene.

Our interest in 'think for yourself' suggests that the ways in which the teacher should intervene might come in this order:

- with empathy, not ridicule
- questioning, to draw attention to reasons why what has been observed may not be the best approach e.g. 'Now then Jetendra, should you be doing it that way? Could you find a better way?'
- questioning to draw-out alternatives and reasons for them
- explanations and instructions to improve the situation.

Why intervene with individuals?

The least used approach by secondary teachers is to talk with small groups, and yet it is common for several students in a class to share the same needs. Teachers can also identify students who arrive first at a 'need to know' situation which others will follow.

Pause before you intervene. Ask yourself whether the intervention would be better with:

- an individual
- a small group
- the whole class

How to intervene – the teacher's style

- Think of yourself as a negotiator
- Make clear the degree of control the student has over which decisions
- Leave as much control as possible with the student

InSET – Building students' independence

Discuss:
One of the features of progression in D&T is the increasing extent to which students are expected to be self-directed in their projects. As students become more independent, teachers need to adopt a greater variety of roles to meet the needs of the students.

Which of these roles have you adopted or would you adopt and in what situation?

Give examples:

Manager	*Advisor*
Negotiator	*Challenger*
Resource provider	*Progress chaser*
Instructor	*Listener*
Facilitator	*Evaluator*
Monitor	*Assessor*

For which of these could responsibility be transferred to:

Nominated students	*Non-teaching assistants*
Technicians	*Peers*

How will these factors change as students progress year-by-year?

Remember: Careful and thorough preparation of equipment will help students to use their time most efficiently.

Discussing these questions as a team will help teachers establish common practices across different D&T areas, so reinforcing the unity of the subject.

Progression

Defining progression

Progression is the 'systematic building of children's knowledge, concepts, skills and attitudes', so as to ensure an orderly advance in their capabilities over a period of time. (DES 1985 *The Curriculum from 5–16*, HMSO)

If only learning were really orderly. In truth it is a messy business which is patchy and partial, moving forward at times, but also falling back.

The features of progression in D&T (outlined in the *Non-Statutory Guidance: Design and Technology Capability*, NCC 1990) include:
* Increased knowledge, skills and understanding
* Moving from familiar to unfamiliar concepts
* Meeting needs which demand more complex or difficult solutions.

To this we might add a fourth – increasing understanding of your own learning and how to progress (metacognition).

Professor Richard Kimbell (March 26th 1994, Workshop address to the Schools Technology team) emphasised the importance of having a goal, 'furious activity alone does not mean progression'. Goals can be defined in terms of what the students are working towards and how skilled they will be at the end.

For example, we would want students to:
* be more skillful than when they started
* know and understand more
* be able to see new goals, to see things that they can intervene in and do
* develop personal autonomy, self directness, the ability to manage themselves and make use of their personal resources.

Whilst the first two goals can be written independently of the student, the last two are not independent of the student and contribute to students achieving personal empowerment.

Kimbell suggests that there are two differing models of progression (on a continuum):
1 The 'Lego' mechanical constructionist view; orderly, linear, increasing in complexity, hierarchical building of capability. Similar to National Curriculum levels of assessment.
2 The 'Organic' model, where an organism grows rather than being built. Here a complex concept is understood at a simple level by a 7 year old, with more depth at 10 years old, building a model of understanding that progressively deepens, eventually providing whole solutions, not parts. The challenge for the teacher is to provide simple examples to explain complex things.

The mechanical model would suggest that students need instruction and activities to develop skills and knowledge before moving onto a designing and making assignment (DMA).

The organic model suggests that activities are vehicles for the learning of skills and knowledge before, during and after the DMA and that these are closely linked to the context. This is, therefore, a more holistic approach. It is important that these activities develop skills and knowledge, and also other process skills such as personal management and thinking for yourself.

It is paramount that DMAs encourage students to grow rather than approach different tasks or problems in the same way, using the same strategies, knowledge and skills repeatedly.

Thus the concept of progression in design and technological capability is characterised as simultaneous development of students'
- propositional knowledge (knowing that . . .)
- tacit knowledge (knowing how . . .)
- process skills.

Propositional knowledge works in conjunction with the tacit knowledge and enhanced process skills to bring all this 'knowledge' to bear in a constructive, purposeful manner. This we refer to as 'capability'.

Progression consists of students' ability to apply this knowledge and these skills to their designing and making and to continuously improving their quality of understanding of their purposes and the outcome.

Some characteristics of progression

Process skills

Autonomy
- The amount and type of teacher intervention/support required or needed.
- Student's ability to plan own work/projects of increasing length and complexity, ability to prepare and follow own design briefs.
- Student's ability to apply the knowledge, skills and understanding gained previously to a new situation or problem.
- Student becoming more effective in working independently and in a variety of group roles – their participation, negotiation, leadership and communication.
- Being able to identify clear targets for personal development in designing and making – recognising where they are and their personal limitations and strengths. Maintaining a good balance between being an active and reflective learner.

Understanding others
- The ability to work beyond the realms of their own personal experience, including wider research to understand others lives/needs, moving from tasks situated in familiar contexts to those in unfamiliar contexts.
- The ability and willingness to address others' needs, as well as their own.

Designerly thinking
- The ability to select and use an increasingly sophisticated range of materials, equipment, processes, skills.
- The extent to which they use their knowledge of materials, equipment, skills and processes to inform their designing and making.
- The ability to clearly identify opportunities for design and technological action to resolve needs.
- The ability to refine and produce a detailed specification of constraints and requirements.
- The ability to identify, consider and cope with a greater number of variables or tasks to be done at any one time, from simple stages, then sequencing, to critical path analysis.
- The ability to take responsibility for considering resource demands – human, physical, costs, time, constraints and opportunities.
- Depth of research and information gathering to inform their designing and making, the appropriateness and complexity of techniques used.
- Student's ability to judge the usefulness of the information gathered for their designing and making.

Judgement
- A student who knows when to, and has the confidence to, move away from familiar designs and answers to problems, and is more creative in their problem-solving.
- Students' use of evaluative techniques to develop quality designs and products evaluating against more complex specifications. Evaluating both process and product. Learning from mistakes. Testing ideas, designs and products against increasingly specific criteria with more stringent testing procedures. Justifying one design over another using increasingly complex or specific criteria in their explanations. Awareness of their value judgements, ethical and moral. The optimising of decisions in the face of increasingly sophisticated recognition of conflicting desires.

Propositional knowledge
Acquiring propositional knowledge
- A student knowing more about materials, production processes and other available technologies.
- A student's development towards industrial/accepted professional practice, e.g. designing to British Standards, using specialist conventions, using technical vocabulary.
- Student's ability to distinguish between designing and making for a single artefact and for manufacturing in bulk production. Having knowledge of techniques of different forms of production.
- Information from other times and cultures, existing products, user needs and preferences.

Using propositional knowledge
- Gathering information to make judgements about the impact of their design – socially, environmentally and economically.
- Application of knowledge and understanding of everyday products to assist designing and making their own ideas.
- A student moving from simple awareness and understanding to application of knowledge and skills, from D&T and other subjects.

Practical skills
- Student's increased skill development through competency to mastery.
- Student's application of new processes and skills, demonstrating increased manual dexterity.
- Recording and communicating ideas, using technical language and specialist techniques. Using a range of presentation styles to achieve purpose.
- The quality of the end product, in terms of skills demonstrated, finish achieved, effectiveness, realistic solution.
- Using skills in ways compatible with his or her technical knowledge, e.g. of materials, tools.

Issues for the teacher

At the centre of the differentiation/progression axes is the student. Progression in learning can only be defined in terms of the individual. Teaching can be structured progressively but individuals will make their own progress route. Teachers need to recognise and allow for this. Learners do not necessarily advance in an orderly manner and we have all witnessed or experienced leaps of understanding when many things 'fall into place' at once.

The teacher should involve students in planning progress in their own learning. Students can be encouraged to take responsibility for their learning and goals should be shared by and with them. It is important to provide opportunities for greater autonomy and negotiation as students become ready, and the only way the teacher knows they are ready is by expecting the student to take the lead and subsequently intervening as necessary.

The teacher holds knowledge vital to a student's individual development; knowledge of 'where they are now' and how best to plan an experience to provide opportunities for progression for the individual as well as the group relies on more or less formal assessment. Done well, this will have the added value of motivating students by matching tasks to capability, thus meeting individual needs.

A major role of the teacher as a facilitator is to provide support to get students to extend themselves further – to recognise the next step, '. . . but why don't you try this as well this time'.

Teachers will be aware of the individual needs of the students and will help students to make judgements on whether this is the time for new knowledge, skills, etc. to be addressed, or the time for consolidation and reinforcement of recently learned skills to take place. A teacher will be sensitive to the right time to challenge students and the time to reassure and build confidence by emphasising the bringing together of all the things they can do already, perhaps to tackle a new task or a new context. For the student this is an opportunity to reflect and consolidate and, of course, it will be more challenging where the task or context is unfamiliar to them.

Later experiences rely on process skills built up in early projects. It is essential to 'work through' design problems with the students, explaining where the thoughts and issues have come from so that the skills of 'designerly thinking' are recognised and can be developed and applied when working on their own. Students need to be aware that these are important skills they are developing and that they will need to use them in later projects.

The teacher needs a view of the whole scheme/curriculum as well as of the year group, ability group, etc. so that opportunities for progression are planned as systematically as possible, rather than achieved in a haphazard manner.

The teacher's role is to define clearly why a project is taught to a particular set of students, to consider its appropriateness, to have clear assessment and record keeping and to map the progress of students.

Simplified understanding/concepts established at early stages must be accurate, so that they do not have to be unlearned and relearned later.

The concept of a 'quality' product is an interesting one – as students may produce a quality product at any level, the nature and expectations of 'quality' changes according to the age and ability of the students. For example, a Y7 student may produce a good yoghurt which is above average for the usual items produced. Could you call it a good quality product? Are quality products only those that meet industry specifications?

Sometimes we do not challenge students enough. We ask them to do the same sort of things, in the same sorts of ways, for the same length of time, but the project topic changes. Progression is about building a level of challenge, competence, confidence, and understanding, which will develop each individual student's capability.

The progression maps which follow give examples of progression in knowledge, understanding and skills for some key areas:
- Design briefs and Challenges
- Food technology
- Managing time

Progression maps for other aspects appear in the year-by-year *Teacher's Resources*.

Building students' skills in dealing with Challenges and design briefs

Design briefs and Challenges can seem very artificial to students. They can seem as if they come from nowhere, whereas for designing to be done well, it relies on students understanding what they are doing and why. Later, when students identify their own tasks, this should resolve itself, but through KS3 we must prepare them for this by revealing the purposes of an assignment both in terms of the designing purposes and the learning purposes. The box on the students' DMA pages labelled *Why this activity is useful* is designed to help with the latter.
- Always explain the reasons for an activity to students – be honest, e.g. if you are restricting the materials they can use because that's all you've got, admit it! It then becomes a valid design constraint.
- Always allow at least some flexibility for students to contribute their own ideas to a task – maximise on this wherever possible.

Year 7	• Take a Challenge and discuss the needs and opportunities it reveals (as a class or in groups). • Look at a selection of these design needs together and talk about how they might be resolved.	• Ask students to underline key words in a design brief. • Examine the context in which the brief originated. • Use role play to explore the context.	• Practise writing a design brief to resolve one of the needs or opportunities revealed.
Year 8	• Visit another area of the school (e.g. cloakrooms/entrance lobby), examine how well it works, then ask students to write a brief to a designer to improve it. • Identify possible design responses and separate them from non-design responses. • Have a video presentation	(e.g. design opportunities in a household kitchen). Discuss to identify different students' perceptions of needs/opportunities, ask students to then write a brief derived from the video. • The brief is presented on behalf of an imaginary client. Put the student in the role of	professional designer. • Use posters and displays to reinforce designing questions, e.g. *Is what you are doing really what is needed? Is there a cheaper way of doing that?* to encourage students to re-appraise a brief continually.
Year 9	• Engage students in short practical problem-solving exercises where students work precisely and only to the given brief (e.g. 'egg races'). • Look at existing products (e.g. how can they be adapted, modified, etc.), students write what they imagine the designer's brief to have been	and then write a revised one for homework which briefs a designer on what improvements are wanted. • Visit locations in the local area that will provide stimuli for identifying needs and opportunities (e.g. a railway station). Then individuals can write a brief to define a task.	• Visit work places for students to see how a company identifies the products it will design and manufacture. • Give students a mini case study of a professional design brief to read for homework. Then give a comprehension test and discuss it next lesson.

NB All the activities suggested for earlier years are worth repeating in a more demanding way in later years.

Managing time – progression map for KS3

The first principles of the RCA STP approach to student time management are:

- Students should learn to take responsibility for their own time management.
- Teachers have to build this skill progressively.
- Communication of information is vital – share your purposes, share your planning.

When introducing a longer activity students should be given a clear idea of the time available for the tasks they have to carry out. If you expect students to finish work on time, keep them well informed, (e.g. is Sports Day going to intrude?) Changes in the time available should be negotiated with the students.

The basic RCA STP approach to starting a DMA is:

The challenge is to . . .

The total time available is . . .

Now let's look at what you are going to do and how long it will take . . .

Skills in time planning and management need to be built up gradually; like any skill, they depend on experience. This means that children need to be continually made aware of their progress in relation to the time available. Moreover a structure is needed to progressively pass the responsibility for time management to the students.

Year 7	**Early terms** • Log time as it is used • Reflect on how time was used • Evaluate how time was used	• Predict how much time will be needed on short tasks (later) **Final term** Within a teacher-controlled	framework, students list/predict/record/evaluate use of time
Year 8	**For any DMA** • Project a list of tasks in advance, in more detail • Project time against each item on list • Have more responsibility for **Lesson-by-lesson** • Negotiate with students to make up time out of lessons when **For longer DMAs** • Re-use end of Y7 framework where students list/predict/record/evaluate use	supplementing core resources • Log time used, reflect and evaluate in-process • At least one short DMA should have a prior FPT on managing time using storyboards – then aims not achieved – voluntary but rewarded with public recognition of time • Teacher leads a review of progress against plans at important stages	students should take responsibility to manage time – reminders from teacher regularly • Gradually increased expectation for students to manage time within the lesson • Publicly negotiated changes of target
Year 9	• Show a better understanding of processes in advance • Group reviews of progress managed less by teacher – student appointed to chair session • Evaluation (and assessment)	stresses completion on time • Gradually increased expectation for students to manage time across a number of lessons including some self-set homework to maintain progress • At least one DMA with prior FPT	on managing time with parallel tasks overlapping – GANNT charts introduced – then students given responsibility to manage time – no reminders from teacher except of that fact

By progressive attention to building time management skills throughout KS3, teachers can rely on most students reaching the responsibilities of KS4 courses with much greater competence. The reward for the teacher is that she or he progressively gains more time to intervene with those students with the greatest remaining needs.

Food Technology – Progression map for KS3

	Skills, Knowledge and Understanding		
	Technical Issues	**Human Interactive Issues**	**Making Issues**
Year 7	• Recognise, group and compare a wide range of foods. • Know about the links between diet and health and understand the main healthy eating recommendations. • Use hygienic practices. • Recognise the working characteristics of basic foods and use them to design products which have a variety of colours, tastes and textures. • Recognise that changes in quantities affect the form and texture of the product, and that changes are caused by combining ingredients in different ways under a variety of temperatures.	• Explore colours, smells and tastes of familiar foods and serve food attractively. • Evaluate the product, consider people's opinions and use appropriate sensory descriptors. • Know about and understand symbolic meanings and uses of food. • Work out the cost of the ingredients for a product.	• Measure foods accurately. • Mix and prepare foods. • Use equipment which allows a degree of precision (e.g. hand whisk/grater). • Select and combine raw, pre-cooked and processed foods to create products. • Make a product to meet a set specification.
Year 8	• Be able to make recommendations and practical adjustments to food and food choice to achieve a healthy diet. • Experiment with ways of combining foods to create and modify products to improve sensory characteristics. • Know that micro-organisms are affected by critical temperatures.	• Know that food choice is affected by nutrition, culture, customs, religion, availability and cost. • Evaluate consumer acceptability of products by using tests with verbal and/or pictorial scale. • Be aware of moral and social issues concerned with product development. • Carry out simple market research as part of product development.	• Know about a range of popular foods from production to consumption and identify the effects of technology at each stage. • Know how to ensure consistency in batch production. • Know about a range or preservation methods and additives and their affect on food. • Match equipment and processes to components being used and outcomes required.
Year 9	• Understand the nature of nutrients and take into account nutritional content of a product in meeting the needs of the users (e.g. DRVs). • Use functional properties of food constituents (protein, starch, fat) to achieve desired effects: shape and textural characteristics of a product (e.g. setting and thickening). • Be able to use food tables and specialist computer programmes to analyse diet and nutritional values of products. • Be aware of product development for larger scale production (manufacturing).	• Understand how social and economic factors influence food choice and diet. • Evaluate food products using difference and attitudinal sensory tests e.g. triangle and hedonic ranking. • Be aware of environmental issues affecting food production, storage and choice of packaging. • Work out the cost of the product and variations to ingredients.	• Select and use processing and cooking methods/equipment to match design intentions. • Generate own design specification. • Sequence steps of food production and processing including safety and hygiene checks (for a small scale production run). • Understand that heat treatment, freezing and additives prolong the shelf life of foods, and apply knowledge of temperature control when storing and working with food.

ASSESSMENT AND THE NATIONAL CURRICULUM

The National Curriculum Order of January 1995 requires students to be assessed against two attainment targets, designing and making. The assessment component of the RCA STP facilitates the required summative, end of key stage, assessment through the ongoing assessment that has taken place in years 7, 8 and 9. This in-course assessment varies in style and method, and sometimes addresses particular components such as skills or underlying knowledge. The end of KS requirement of the NC for a summation of students overall D&T capability is not sufficient for students, their parents or the school, all of whom need continuous feedback on each student's pattern of progress. And teachers themselves, for their own purposes, need to assess each student regularly.

Mapping NC requirements against the Project's approach to assessment

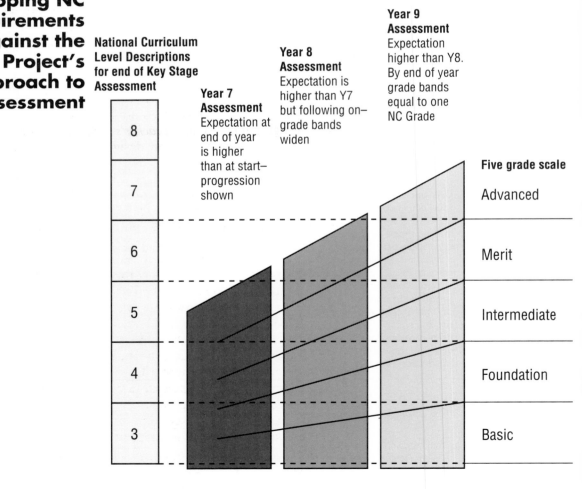

Figure 17: Assessment in the RCA STP course

1 Students' designing and making work is assessed against a five point grade scale. The grades have been assigned the labels: Basic, Foundation, Intermediate, Merit and Advanced, although Schools may choose to use A–E.

2 In the light of research from organisations such as the Goldsmiths College (University of London) Technology Education Research Unit (TERU) we have initially set the range for Y7 across levels 3–5 of the National Curriculum.

3 Teachers working with selected groups of students may find there is a need to adapt this Y7 range to reflect the ability of their students.

4 The grade boundaries for the end of Y7 are higher than at the start of the year indicating expectations that students will progress over a year's work.

5 Students' widening range of progress through KS3 leads to a widening of grade boundaries to maintain the five grade structure.

6 By the end of KS3 the grade boundaries are equal to National Curriculum levels matching summative KS3 level descriptions.

The RCA STP assessment scheme

Diagnostic assessment

A main objective of the RCA STP is to help develop capable, autonomous students in D&T. In achieving this aim, assessment is a vital diagnostic tool that will be used to:

- identify what students are learning and the rate at which they are progressing
- identify students' strengths so that positive achievement can be rewarded and extension or enrichment tasks provided
- identify students' weaknesses so that remedial action may be taken
- analyse the programme of study to determine its suitability for the students following it.

The key features of the RCA STP assessment scheme are:

1 It is differentiated to allow all students to show positive achievements and progression. The *Teacher's Resource* for each year has differentiated statements for designing and making that facilitate assessment of both the process and outcome in each attainment target for each DMA. These are sub-divided into 'sub-statements' to illustrate that there is a valid range of ways that students can demonstrate achievement within a level (see figures 18 and 19). Students are graded, however, on the basis of best fit within a level, they do not need to satisfy every sub-statement indicated for that level.

2 The assessment scheme facilitates students taking responsibility for their learning and its assessment. Student self-assessment is encouraged at all stages of the designing and making Challenge. In the *To be successful* statements students are made aware of success criteria before they begin work on a project. Many of these prompts provide criteria by which students evaluate aspects of their work. The project's view is that a thorough understanding of evaluation is the key to self-assessment. The process must be reinforced by teacher-student negotiation to develop these prompts as a basis for students to evaluate the process and outcomes of their work. Students and teachers are encouraged to record their assessment or evaluation on the same sheet (see figure supplied in the *Teacher's Resource*).

3 It caters for differing forms of assessment. Written tests, teacher observation, peer group, quality of artefact, and self-evaluation are included. As noted, student self-assessment and evaluation are a core part of the philosophy. Different forms of assessment allow

students to reveal their differing component strengths, and research into gender differences have shown that girls and boys generally perform better in different forms of assessment. Suggestions for using different forms of assessment are given in the *Teacher's Resources* along with the designing and making statements.

4 Assessment is integral to all work being undertaken. The *To be successful* box establishes assessment as central from the start of every DMA.

5 It provides students with a clear understanding of the criteria by which their performance will be assessed. The *To be successful* box is carefully written in student-friendly language and provides the initial prompt to look at what will constitute a quality process or outcome in a project. The use of student and teacher assessment sheets will facilitate the process of student-teacher dialogue throughout the course.

6 Students will become familiar with the approach to assessment in D&T throughout their secondary schooling. The RCA STP aims to build increasing student responsibility for many activities. Assessment is one of those which is targeted in Y7. The philosophy is simple: if we wish to have autonomous students by the examination years, post-14, we must start working towards this as early as possible. As with time management, much responsibility will lie with the teacher in the early stages but, with persistence and openness, students will become progressively more able to handle their own assessment with accuracy.

7 It provides members of a D&T Faculty with a benchmark against which internal moderation can be measured. If a consistent level of assessment is to be achieved across this diverse subject, attention must be paid to internal moderation. The level descriptions for each DMA provided in the *Teacher's Resources* are a starting point for this process. Two strategies that may help colleagues focus on these issues are described below.

InSET – Collecting evidence of D&T capability

- What tangible evidence has been produced in your students' most recent D&T activity, *e.g. sketches, written work, models, final outcomes?*
- What does this evidence tell you about how and why it was produced, *e.g. What were the students' intentions? How did the pupils try to achieve these?*

- How could you involve students in keeping simple records of how they went about their work, *e.g. sketch books, diaries, tape recordings?*
- What strategies do you adopt for recording ephemeral evidence? How do you value this in comparison to tangible evidence?

InSET – Establishing standards

- With a colleague, consider D&T outcomes produced recently by a student that you teach. Discuss the level descriptions that you consider were satisfied during the activities. Which level do you consider overall best fits the achievement of that student? What evidence did you use other than the outcome of the project?

DMA

Area(s) of study

To be successful

Assessment focuses	Teaching focuses

Designing statements Advanced	Making statements Advanced
Intermediate	**Intermediate**
Basic	**Basic**

Key statements are starred (*)

Figure 18: Blank assessment criteria sheet

DMA	Novelty Chocolates

Area(s) of Study	food/plastics

To be successful (from student book)

You must be able to say why you chose your event or company.

Select a suitable design for it from a number of ideas.

Draw your final design accurately and make the mould precisely.

Choose the type of chocolate and melt it carefully so that it gives you the best result for your design – the quality of your novelty is important.

Create a package which will *both* protect the chocolate well and display it attractively.

Assessment focuses

Designing – for an event or company:
- to the constraints of working with chocolate and plastics as materials
- to produce a number of designs which can be evaluated against simple criteria.

Making:
- to a high level of accuracy, hygiene and finish
- with as little waste as possible
- with concern for the presentation of the finished product.

Teaching focuses

To introduce students to the different D&T areas, linking them.

To work with different materials within a single project.

To teach how the properties of a material affect the way that it can be used (chocolate/plastics).

To introduce the safe usage of a range of standard D&T machinery or equipment.

To establish expectations in quality of work.

Designing statements   Advanced

The design folio:
- makes the fullest use of drawing and models*
- demonstrates understanding of the properties of chocolate and plastics
- contains a number of quality designs* which are linked to the chosen event, and evaluated to show this.

Good final design and reasons for its choice.

Making statements   Advanced

The finished chocolate novelty is:
- made to a high standard of accuracy*
- made with very little wastage of materials
- evaluated to show how these properties have been achieved and how they could have been improved
- packaged to both protect and display the novelty*

Intermediate

The design folio:
- includes drawings and/or models*
- demonstrates understanding of the properties of either chocolate or plastics.

A number of alternative designs are offered which have a link to the identified event*.

A final design is shown with reasonable accuracy.

Intermediate

The finished chocolate novelty:
- is made in a planned manner to an adequate quality with accuracy evident
- is evaluated to show where faults have occurred and simple changes that could be made to improve the product.

Basic

The design folio includes:
- sketches with some clarity or vitality
- realistic ways for producing the novelty
- some understanding of the principles of melting chocolate or vacuum-forming safety.
- A final design proposal.

Basic

The finished chocolate novelty:
- is made suitably for the original design intention
- is made to a reasonable level of success including accuracy
- is evaluated to identify simple changes that could be made to improve an aspect of the finished product.

©1995 The Royal College of Art Schools Technology Project

Key statements are starred (*)

Figure 19: Sample assessment criteria sheet for a DMA

Student's name		Class	
Project			
Challenge			

To be successful | S | T

My design will:

When I make it I will:

Designing achievements | S | T

I am most proud of these features of my designing:

Teacher's Comments

Making achievements | S | T

I am most proud of these features of my making:

Teacher's Comments

Final Grade for Designing   Student ☐
                             Teacher ☐

Final Grade for Making   Student ☐
                          Teacher ☐

©1995 The Royal College of Art Schools Technology Project

Figure 20: Sample teacher/student assessment sheet

Assessing capability in D&T

A capable student is one able to reflect whilst taking actions and to act on their reflections. Capable students work iteratively, that is, to-ing and fro-ing between the need to confront reality and question validity. (TERU 1993)

D&T capability is much more than the sum of its constituent parts; knowledge, understanding, and designing and making skills. It is made manifest when students are given the opportunity to undertake appropriate designing and making activities (DMAs). It is within such a framework that students are able to demonstrate their ability to draw on knowledge, skill and understanding; in other words to display their full capability.

Evidence of capability can be extremely diverse. To ensure that it is valued and recorded we recommend that students are encouraged from the start of KS3 to keep all stages of their work and to build this into a portfolio of evidence of capability.

Their D&T teacher is paramount in helping students to recognise their growing capability, and to demonstrate it. For the folio to reveal accurately a student's capability at any given time there will need to be a great deal of teacher–pupil interaction. Every such interaction is a time when teachers will be making assessment of students' capability. These assessments do not need to be formal and do not necessarily involve recording on every occasion, but it is crucial that they form a significant part of the communication between student and teacher.

The Project has adopted a five point scale of achievement (figure 17). One reason for this is the realisation that students do not necessarily develop capability in a simple linear manner. Another is the fact that many students will take a year or more to progress through a National Curriculum level. Even with the extra discrimination afforded by five grades, students in Y7 and Y8 will fluctuate in their performance and their designing and making grades may not show a smooth continuity.

Assessment and yearly school reports

The Education Act of 1988 requires schools to make an annual report to parents on the attainment of their students. Any teacher using this course should have a wealth of evidence available to them from which to produce a report. The reporting procedures of different schools are obviously a matter for each institution but we would suggest the following model which has many desirable features. (See *Teacher's Resource*.)

Designing
Global statement (level description) for the level of achievement in this attainment target

Making
Global statement (level description) for the level of achievement in this attainment target

Free-form response from teacher to cover aspects such as attendance, attitude, etc.

PULLING D&T TOGETHER

Students will only see D&T as a single subject if the staff who teach them also see it this way. There is much that teachers can do to draw attention to techniques and approaches that the areas contributing to D&T have in common. This will not only avoid unnecessary repetition in the students' learning experience, but will also prevent potential conflict between different learning styles and approaches to the subject which may confuse students. Common approaches and practices will help students to make steady progress and improve the overall results of the course.

At the heart of this is continuity. Rotational arrangements are generally a disaster and the reasons for this give us some valuable pointers. The most important reason is that students do not perceive any lines of continuity across the different areas. When they move to a new area with a different teacher they start afresh, as if they were beginning a new subject rather than building on what they have learnt already. This means, of course, that progression in their learning does not take place or occurs in a very uneven way.

Given the expertise of contributing teachers and the rapidly expanding nature of technological knowledge and capability, it is unlikely that individuals will bring sufficient depth and enthusiasm to the whole National Curriculum D&T spectrum. It is therefore necessary for teachers responsible for D&T at KS3 and beyond to collaborate. What, then, must they do to ensure continuity and progression for their students despite the variety of skills, techniques and traditions they bring? We propose five areas of common ground on which this can be built:

1 Designing and learning processes

The designing process always operates under constraints specific to a particular product or situation. It is therefore not possible to identify a single designing process. However, we can identify common features in the ways people respond to particular design needs and how they bring products to realisation. Unfortunately, teachers have to identify these factors largely for themselves. There are models of design processes but, by their very nature, models do not tell the whole story and are open to misuse and misinterpretation.

The four attainment targets in the first National Curriculum Orders set out aspects of designing which are common, but unfortunately these were seen by some as representing an orderly sequence. Some teachers, with little experience of designing, encouraged their students to follow the sequence rigidly, even portraying 'Evaluation' as a final stage rather than as an aspect of designing which permeates the whole process.

InSET – Looking at learning processes

Meet to assess the work of two students in one D&T area – a high and a middle achiever. Discuss these questions:
- *What learning processes did they follow, in what order, and why?*
- *In what ways were these similar to, and different from, practices by students in other D&T areas?*

2 Common vocabulary and language

Different D&T related professionals are quite happy not to share vocabulary as they are not expected to work together. Food technologists talk of ingredients and recipes, electronic engineers of components and specifications, and building designers call themselves architects and do not call the results of their work products.

By contrast, teachers working to the National Curriculum Orders cross professional designers' boundaries and have to try to draw out what is common across their activities so that children can make sense of them. Without cross-relating the different terminologies this cannot be done.

InSET – Understanding how others work

On a regular basis, visit an area where a member of the D&T team carries out one of the regular technical demonstrations they do for students. Comment on what is similar in their area to yours and how things differ. NB: This will also help you to find out more about what goes on in a parallel area.

3 Approaches to materials, components and ingredients

The RCA STP approach places emphasis on what is common in the use of materials, components and ingredients. For example, the Y7 students' book links activities on the casting of aluminium, jellies and chocolate to push home the underlying concept of changing the state of materials to form them into products. Similarly, students develop their understanding of the nature of materials further if, for example, they recognise that you can use different means of heating materials to bring them to a mouldable state, and that different materials can hold a stable state for a number of reasons. Also, there are common reasons why we use bulk-manufactured ingredients in a food or components in an electronic circuit.

InSET – Common strands across D&T

What is common in the internal structure of bread, sponge cakes, Styrofoam, Celcon blocks and wood? How does their structure give them strength? How is this structure created? What are the implications of grain structure for the ways we use wood, thick card, felts and glass reinforcement mats? How do woven materials differ from these?

4 Broad attitudes to techniques

Teachers can and should draw out common techniques and methods even when the terminology is not shared. In this sense, jam is referred to as the adhesive holding marzipan to a cake just as PVA holds plywood and its veneer together. This aids understanding of why neither works as well if too much adhesive is used.

Differences are also important. Why do we have different saws for different materials? Why is card cut in the same way as pastry (with a knife on a special board) whereas aluminium sheet is cut like a textile (with shears or scissors).

5 Common routine practices

Just as there are common aspects of design processes occurring in different D&T areas so these can be dealt with in common ways. Whilst dealing with these in more similar ways may not change much by itself, the underlying message will be strong – this is one subject.